Jeanne Dugas of Acadia

by Cassie Deveaux Cohoon

Copyright © 2013 - Cassie Deveaux Cohoon

This book is a work of fictionalized history. Most of the characters, places and events depicted are based on historical research, but are dramatized for literary consumption. Some
characters are products of the author's imagination.

All rights reserved. No part of this work may be reproduced or used
in any form or by any means, electronic or mechanical, including photocopying, recording or any information storage or retrieval
system, without the prior written permission of the publisher. Cape
Breton University Press recognizes fair dealing exceptions under Access Copyright. Responsibility for the opinions, research and the
permissions obtained for this publication rests with the author.

Cape Breton University Press recognizes
the support of the Canada Council for the
Arts, Block Grant program, and the Province of Nova Scotia, through the De-
partment of Communities, Culture and
Heritage, for our publishing program.
We are pleased to work in partnership
with these bodies to develop and promote our cultural resources.

Cover image: From photos by Heidi Moses, Fortress of Louisbourg
Author photo by Tim Snow
Cover Design: Cathy MacLean Design, Pleasant Bay, NS
Layout: Mike Hunter, Port Hawkesbury and Sydney, NS
First printed in Canada

Library and Archives Canada Cataloguing in Publication
Cohoon, Cassie Deveaux, 1935-
Jeanne Dugas of Acadia : a novel / Cassie Deveaux Cohoon.
Includes bibliographical references.
ISBN 978-1-897009-71-0
1. Dugas, Jeanne, 1731-1817--Fiction. 2. Acadians--Fiction.
3. Chéticam (N.S.)--Fiction. I. Title.
PS8605.O379J42 2013 C813'.6 C2013-901290-7

Cape Breton University Press
P.O. Box 5300
Sydney, Nova Scotia B1P 6L2
Canada
www.cbupress.ca

Jeanne Dugas
of Acadia

by Cassie Deveaux Cohoon

Cape Breton University Press
Sydney, Nova Scotia, Canada

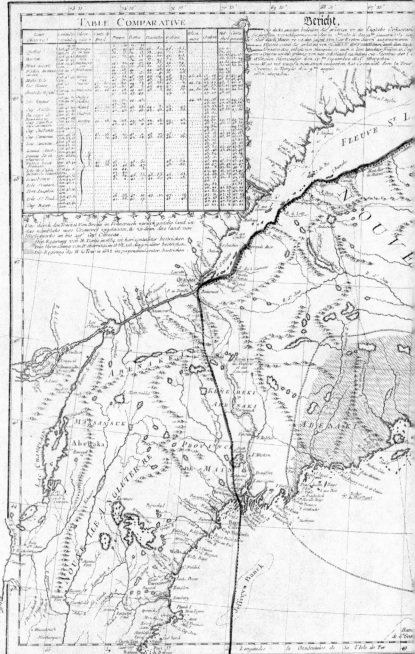

Explication

Le pais Concedé par Cromwel aux S.t laTour Croisne et compte le 9. Aoust 1656, est entouré d'un double trait fin ....

Le pais restitué par le traite de Breda est le même que celui qui avoit été Concedé par Cromwel et en
outre le pais depuis Merliguesche, jusqu'a Canceau.

Le Gouvernement du S.t Denis en 1654 est haché horisontalement.

Le Gouvernem.t du S.r Charnizei en 1633 est haché diagonalement.

Le Gouvernem.t du S.r la Tour en 1655 est haché perpendiculairement.

GOLFE DE
S.t LAURENT

L A B R A D O R

GASPES

Baye Miramuski

Isles de la Madelaine

ISLE ROYALE

Banc de l'Isle de Sable

Browns Banck

Note

We did, in my opinion most inhumanly, and upon pretences that in the eye of an honest man are not worth a farthing, root out this poor, innocent, deserving people, whom our utter inability to govern or to reconcile gave us no sort of right to extirpate.

Edmund Burke (1729-1797)
British statesman, on the Deportation of the Acadians

J eanne felt strange as she twirled gently in her new, and first, French-style gown. Strange but excited, as if the dress were a visible aspect of the changes she felt inside.

It was the Feast Day of Sainte-Anne, July 26, 1744. Jeanne Dugas and her family were celebrating the completion of her studies at the convent of the Congrégation de Notre-Dame, in Louisbourg on Île Royale. Jeanne was thirteen-and-a-half years old and now considered to be "a proper young lady."

The gown was made of beautiful cornflower blue silk and she wore it over a white linen chemise. The tight bodice was closed with fabric bows and the skirt fell over a hoop underskirt. Delicate lace edged the large white collar and the sleeves of the chemise that showed below the blue sleeves of the gown. Her dark brown hair was done up in a chignon and covered with a modest white cap edged in the same lace. A blue and green bead choker complemented the ensemble.

Jeanne did not have the delicate beauty of her older sister, Angélique – she had a beauty all her own. Her features were strong and pleasing, her look direct and serious. She twirled again and smiled to herself.

3

—

Maman and Jeanne's stepfather, Monsieur de la Tour, had been very surprised when Jeanne asked for a French-style gown for her celebration. It was what Angélique would have wanted but not, typically, Jeanne. Jeanne had always insisted on wearing traditional Acadian dress – a linen chemise under a dark-coloured vest, a striped linen skirt, a bonnet and often a neck scarf. Maman and Monsieur de la Tour were visibly pleased at Jeanne's choice for this occasion.

As plans were being made to celebrate Jeanne's rite of passage on the Feast of Sainte-Anne, Maman had taken Jeanne to a fashionable boutique just beside Le Billard tavern. It sold fabrics imported from France, along with drawings and patterns for the latest styles worn by the elite in Paris.

Jeanne's brother Joseph was obviously pleased with the plans, but he did not tease her. It seemed lately as if he was more often treating her as an adult rather than a little sister. He asked her what colour she had chosen for her gown and, a few days before the big day, he gave her a delicate choker made with small blue and green beads.

"They tell me this is what fashionable ladies are wearing in France," he said.

Jeanne beamed at the sight of the beautiful necklace. It would be perfect with her gown.

And now the big day was here. Joseph, his wife Marguerite, and their children had arrived to join the others at the de la Tour home. Their brother Charles was here too, on a visit from Grand-Pré. They were all in the parlour waiting for Jeanne. As she walked into the room, Jeanne felt rather than heard a gasp. There was a brief silence, as if they were unsure what to say, or if they should say anything at all. But Joseph could not help himself. "Jeanne, you are beautiful!" he said. She blushed, but she was clearly pleased.

First they went to the Chapelle Saint-Louis, at the garrison of Louisbourg, to attend a special mass in honour of Sainte-Anne. As the de la Tours and the Dugas walked to the front of the Chapelle, Jeanne could not help but feel proud. She did feel a twinge of guilt as they passed the people crowded at the rear – many of them Acadians and many obviously poor – but today was her day.

After mass, they hurried to Le Billard. The owner, Marguerite Dugas the widow Beauséjour, had closed the tavern for the day and invited her relatives and a few Acadian friends for the mid-day dinner. She was the cousin of Jeanne's late father, Joseph Dugas. Monsieur de la Tour had provided some excellent French wine from his own cellar, and Jeanne had her first glass of grown-up wine. After the meal, they went out into the streets to take in the public celebrations for the remainder of the day and into the evening.

—

Returning to the de la Tour home, all agreed that it had been a wonderful celebration of both Sainte-Anne and Jeanne, as well as of the fortunes of war thus far. But Monsieur de la Tour was cautious in his toast to the colony of Île Royale, reminding them of the tensions between France and Britain and that their fate as Acadians hung in the balance.

Before falling asleep that night, Jeanne reviewed the events of the day in her mind. It was a habit she had formed as a very little girl when she had first become aware that things were not always as they appeared. She knew that there were many layers to life in Louisbourg. The people who so joyously celebrated the Feast Day of Sainte-Anne knew very well that the French and the British were once again at war in Europe.

They knew that their happiness and well-being could disappear in a puff of smoke. Still wrapped in the warm glow of her celebration, Jeanne knew that if Louisbourg fell, she and her family would be among those most in peril, no matter what her brother Joseph told her.

———

A few days after the celebration, Joseph brought an artist to the house on rue de l'Étang to paint a portrait of Jeanne in her beautiful blue gown. Joseph asked the artist to make the portrait small.

"So we can carry it easily if we have to leave Louisbourg," he explained to Jeanne.

Part 1
An Acadian
Family

Paspébiac

Fleuve Saint-Lauren

Gaspé

Ristigouche

La Petite Rochelle
Baie des Chaleurs

Nipisiguit

Chipagon

ÎLES DE LA MADELEINE
Havre Hébert

Miramichi Bay and area
Camp de l'Espérance

(ÎLE SAINT-JEAN)
PRINCE EDWARD ISLAND

Richibuctu

(NEW BRUNSWICK)

Chétican .

CAP BRETON
(ÎLE ROYALE)

Magré

Shediac

Port-la-Joye

Sainte-Anne (Fredericton)

Miré

Jemseg

Isthmus of
Chignecto

Tatamagouche

Louisbourg

Rivière
Saint-Jean

Beaubassin

Remshic

Chédabuctou
Cobequid (Truro)

Port Toulouse/Potlotek
Nēireishak

NE

St. Croix
(river and island)

Baie Française

Les Mines
Grand-Pré

Minas Basin

ÎLE MADAME
Canceau

Port Royal

(NOVA SCOTIA)

Annapolis Basin

Annapolis

Chezzetcook

Halifax

SABLE ISLAND

Clare

Saint Mary's Bay

La Have

Pubnico

Cap de Sable

Chapter 1

Sometimes Maman grew annoyed with her when she insisted on the fact that she, Jeanne, was Acadian. Maman had
said to her once, "Jeanne, you were born here in Louisbourg,
and that means that you are French."

"No," she had replied stubbornly, "if all of you are Acadian then I am Acadian too."

It was a question that truly vexed her and brought out
her stubbornness and determination, even when she was very
little. Joseph, at least, agreed with her.

"Ah well," Joseph said, "the Acadians are known for being
têtu."

"Well, there you are," she had replied, stamping her foot
and wondering why everyone found this so amusing.

—

Jeanne Dugas's forebears were one of the families that founded
Acadia in the first half of the 1600s. Europeans had fished the
area as early as the late 1400s – Portuguese, Basques, Normans
and Bretons. At first they would cross the ocean in the spring,
salt their catch of fish on board ship, and return to Europe
in the fall without touching land. Later, some of them set up

temporary fishing outposts on land for the duration of the fishing season, but they always returned to Europe in the fall. When contact was made with the Mi'kmaw people, a profitable trade in beaver fur was also developed, and European countries vigorously sought to exploit these riches.

In 1604, a certain Pierre du Gua, Sieur de Mons, set sail for that new world. The king of France had given him a grant that bestowed on him exclusive fishing and fur-trading rights over a large territory. The grant was given on the condition that he settle and cultivate the land and convert the Native people to Catholicism. The new colony was referred to as "La Cadie." One of the men on Sieur de Mons's two ships was Samuel de Champlain, a navigator and mapmaker.

They spent their first winter on Île Sainte-Croix in the Baie Française, where they almost perished from scurvy and the cold. The following summer they chose a site on the rivière Dauphin, where they built a comfortable shelter. Most importantly, they became friends with the Mi'kmaq, who welcomed them and taught them how to survive in La Cadie. The Frenchmen learned how to cure scurvy by boiling the bark and leaves of evergreen trees to make a kind of tea. They learned what crops could be grown, how to hunt the animals and how to cope with the climate. They formed an alliance with the Mi'kmaq that would last for more than 150 years.

At about the same time as Acadia was growing, the British established colonies of their own, farther south along the coast, and the ancient rivalry between France and Britain on the European continent was continued in the new world. Over the next hundred years, the land of Acadia would change hands ten times between the French and the British, either through victory in war or by negotiation. For the British, to have control of Acadia was a strategic ploy. It protected their colonies along the north Atlantic coast and guaranteed the freedom of the shipping lanes for commerce. When the British were in charge, they did not bring in many settlers, at least not in the early days.

So it was really the French who settled and developed the colony of Acadia. In the 1640s, they began a system of dykes to drain the salt marshes near Port Royal and turn them into rich farmland. In the 1670s, a new community was settled in Grand-Pré in the Minas Basin area and another system of dykes put in place. Other communities followed.

When the French were in control, they had their own authorities. There was a governor, the military and of course the clergy. When the British were in control, the French elites had to leave, but the British, without a large influx of their own settlers, were dependent on the Acadians for locally grown food and meat. By and large, the two peoples accommodated each other. A system of Acadian deputies was created, whereby a delegate from each Acadian community was charged with dealing with the British governor, receiving orders and making the Acadians' needs known. The success of this system sometimes depended on the disposition of the British governor, but it worked well for some time.

By the early 1700s, Acadia had been under the control of the French since the signing of the Treaty of Bréda in 1667, and this period was a kind of golden age for the French settlers. They prospered for generations and were now their own people – Acadians.

The French settlers would originally have come from different areas of France, perhaps have spoken different dialects, have worn different styles of clothing, have had different loyalties. But over time they had become one people: Acadians, a colony of farmers who owned their own land. They were prosperous in a way they could not have been in France. And they had a certain amount of freedom, whether ruled by France or Britain.

—

Then, in 1710, the British recaptured Port Royal, and the Treaty of Utrecht, signed in 1713, handed over all of Acadia to the British; the English renamed it Nova Scotia. The French retained Cap Breton and Île Saint-Jean, together renamed the colony of Île Royale.

France also lost its fishing settlement in Placentia, Newfoundland, and proceeded to establish a fishing outport on Île Royale with some French fishermen and entrepreneurs from Placentia and Saint-Pierre et Miquelon. They named the new outport Louisbourg after the French king. The French authorities encouraged Acadians to emigrate to Île Royale.

Chapter 2

Jeanne's parents, Joseph Dugas and Marguerite Richard, were both Acadians – he born in Port Royal in 1690, she in Grand-Pré in 1694. They met in Grand-Pré and were married there in January 1711. Their first son, Charles, was born in December of the same year.

Joseph Dugas was a landowner, carpenter, caboteur or coastal navigator and trader. He was one of a new class in Acadia, owning land, but not tied to it to earn a living. With his own schooner he could move about independently. Carpentry was also a portable trade, and a respected one.

Joseph was one of the young Acadians who worried about the political situation, and his fears were confirmed when Port Royal fell to the English in the autumn of 1710. The mother country, France, had sent very little assistance to the Acadians for that battle, and Joseph was bitter but realistic. Unlike his parents' generation, he did not believe that the Acadian settlers would now continue to prosper under British rule.

Joseph's family was a prominent, close-knit one and he considered himself a man of some substance. But he had told Marguerite of his misgivings about the political situation before they married and warned her that if she joined her life to his, she must be prepared to follow him. And now, he was determined to leave Acadia, a decision not as difficult for him as for those restricted to farming.

———

In 1714, twenty-four-year-old Joseph made arrangements to leave his land in the care of relatives in Grand-Pré before setting sail on his two-masted schooner, the *Sainte-Anne*, to resettle his family on Île Royale. With him were his wife and their two little sons Charles and Joseph fils, the latter still an infant at his mother's breast. Joseph also persuaded his father, Abraham, to leave with him. The French authorities were offering a stipend to Acadian settlers to encourage them to move to Île Royale and Joseph Dugas accepted it, leaving his property in Acadia under the care of his brother, Abraham fils.

Their destination was Port Toulouse, on the southeast corner of Île Royale, on the neck of land that separated the Bras d'Or Lake from the Atlantic Ocean. An earlier French settlement, known as Saint-Pierre, had flourished there in the 17th century, but was destroyed by fire and abandoned. The area had some farmland and, although it was not as rich as that of Acadia, it had attracted some farmers. Joseph knew the area well because of his activities as a caboteur. As the fishing outport at Louisbourg grew to become the capital of Île Royale in the following years, Port Toulouse also grew into an important community, attracting farmers and fishermen, navigators, coastal traders, shipbuilders and loggers.

Many years later, Marguerite would confess to her daughter Jeanne that when she arrived at Port Toulouse on a cool, grey, overcast day in June of 1714, her heart sank. Living conditions were clearly not what she had been used to in Acadia – now called Nova Scotia. The few habitations were very primitive, consisting of simple vertical log construction, nothing like the solid houses they were used to in Grand-Pré. Most of them were one storey; just a few were a storey-and-a-half. Some had fenced-in yards where farm animals were kept and a few vegetables and herbs were grown. The habitations were close to the water's edge and a cold dampness penetrated both the houses and their inhabitants.

Much of Île Royale was rocky, with a thick forest cover. It was easy to see why most Acadians did not want to sacrifice their prosperous farms for this undeveloped land, and there were no salt marshes that could be converted to fertile farms as had been done in Acadia.

Of course there was no time for fussing. The Dugas were welcomed and sheltered by the few people already in Port Toulouse. A simple dwelling was quickly erected and they unpacked the belongings they had brought with them from Grand-Pré. Finding his young wife in tears at the end of their first week in Port Toulouse, Joseph Dugas promised her that one day he would provide her with a home she would be proud of.

—

This southwest coast of Cap Breton had once been a strategic area for the French authorities, and after 1713 they quickly sought to re-establish a settlement there, which they named Port Toulouse. It was the closest habitation to the now-British territory of Nova Scotia, making it important from a military standpoint.

The area was well known to the Mi'kmaq, who called it Potlotek. For centuries the Mi'kmaq had portaged their canoes over a narrow isthmus to the Bras d'Or Lake and used the area as a meeting place. In the summer months they made their base by the ocean on the Port Toulouse side and in the winter they camped inland on the Bras d'Or.

The French had persuaded the Mi'kmaq to adopt the Catholic religion, and they assigned a French missionary to live among them on a year-round basis. In 1713, Father Antoine Gaulin, a priest from the Séminaire de Missions Étrangères in Québec, established a mission for the Mi'kmaq at Malagawatch at the site of one of their traditional gathering places. The Mi'kmaq had become allies of the French against the British, and the French maintained relations with them.

—

For the energetic, ambitious Joseph Dugas, Île Royale was a land of opportunity. He quickly established trading contracts with the recently opened fishing outport at Louisbourg, transporting firewood and lumber there from Port Toulouse. He also carried firewood, livestock and other freight between Cap Breton and Île Saint-Jean, and even to and from Nova Scotia, although it was officially forbidden to trade with the British. Within two years he was no longer in need of the French stipend to help support his family and, in 1717, he acquired ownership of a considerable acreage of land in the area of Port Toulouse. A few years later, he had built himself a new schooner, the *Marie-Josèphe*. He wanted to name it the *Marguerite* after his wife, but she had refused.

By 1723, Joseph Dugas and Marguerite were well established, and their family was growing. They now had six children: Charles, Joseph and four little daughters born in Port Toulouse – Marie Madeleine, Marguerite, Anne and Angélique. Two hired hands and one servant brought the Dugas household to eleven. Sadly, Grandfather Abraham had passed away during his second winter in Port Toulouse.

By this time, thirteen Acadian families had settled there and living conditions had improved, although they were far from the comforts many had known in Acadia.

Now, Joseph Dugas was thinking of moving his family to Louisbourg, where there would be more business opportunities, and where he knew his wife Marguerite would find life more comfortable. In 1723 he was contracted to build a double house there for a blacksmith, Dominique Detcheverry. The house was on rue Royalle, in a good part of Louisbourg. When Detcheverry had problems paying for the construction, he agreed to give Joseph one half of the house in payment for his work. Marguerite was happy with the move; she had found the years in Port Toulouse very difficult.

—

Since 1713, the fishing outport of Louisbourg had grown very quickly. It not only exploited the rich cod fishery but had become an important trading and transhipment centre, and a strategic base in the area. By 1720, the French authorities had started a twenty-five-year fortification program to turn the outport into a fortress. It quickly became a busy, bustling community.

In the summer of 1726, Joseph Dugas sailed from Port Toulouse to Louisbourg on the *Marie-Josèphe*, with Marguerite and their family, which now included another son, Abraham, just a few weeks old. Joseph's other schooner, the *Sainte-Anne*, sailed with them, manned by others of his crew. The following year, he bought a third schooner, the *Hangoit*.

The new Dugas home was larger than the one in Port Toulouse. It was made with a heavy timber frame called charpente construction, with vertical piquet wall fill that came from the forest near the fortress. One room was used as a carpentry workshop. The furniture was ordinary and rather worn. Although the Dugas family was not part of the elite in the Governor's circle at the garrison, Joseph Dugas was a respected craftsman and caboteur, and they had the means to live comfortably.

The Dugas had brought with them one servant and the crew from the schooners. Soon after they arrived, they acquired a black slave named Pierre Josselin. Marguerite treated him like one of the family and he responded to her kindness. He was very good with the children. Unmarried members of the ships' crews also stayed at the Dugas house when they were in port.

The Dugas family continued to prosper and grow and, in 1728, they acquired the other half of the Detcheverry house. Their eighth child, a son named Étienne, was born in the winter of 1729, but he died a few months before his second birthday. Jeanne, their ninth and last child, was born in the house on rue Royalle in 1731. Soon after that the busy, happy life on rue Royalle was disrupted.

—

In 1732, smallpox spread through Louisbourg. This was not so unusual, but by 1733 it reached epidemic proportions and brought with it the threat of starvation. The Dugas household was not immediately affected and Marguerite hoped and prayed that they would be spared, but late in 1732 her daughters Marie Madeleine and Marguerite died. The following winter the epidemic claimed Anne and Joseph père, as well as the slave Josselin, who was only twenty-five years old.

Marguerite had difficulty coming to terms with the death of her husband, and the loss of her three little daughters left a big void in her heart. Joseph had been the solid centre of her life – so alive, so vigorous and hard-working. Jeanne, who was barely two years old when her father died, had only one memory of this time – of her mother clutching her and her sister Angélique to her bosom as if she were afraid they too would be taken from her. Years later, when Jeanne herself had lost children, she understood her mother's anguish.

Marguerite Richard, the widow Dugas, was left with three sons, Charles, Joseph and Abraham, and two daughters, Angélique and Jeanne. But she was not destitute. As well as her home on rue Royalle, she owned two schooners, and had two domestic servants and four sailors as part of her household. There was also the land in Grand-Pré and Port Toulouse.

According to the custom of the time, male children were considered minors until the age of twenty-five. Marguerite was therefore elected to be tuteur to her three sons and François Cressonet dit Beauséjour was elected as subrogé tuteur, to assist her. He was the husband of Marguerite Dugas, a cousin of Jeanne's father. The Cressonets owned the fashionable Le Billard tavern.

Jeanne kept only a vague memory of the house on rue Royalle, because three years after her father's death, when she was only five, her mother Marguerite remarried. This event brought a big change to all their lives.

Chapter 3

There was a scarcity of women in the growing community of Louisbourg. Marguerite Richard, the widow Dugas, was still of childbearing age and, with her house and commercial activities, she had good prospects. In fact, she made a very fine match indeed.

She married Charles de Saint-Étienne de la Tour, the great-grandson of *the* Charles de Saint-Étienne de la Tour, one of the founders of Acadia and its first governor. It was a proud name with a proud heritage. Marguerite's new husband was also a caboteur, as Joseph had been. He was a friend of the Dugas family, and had been godfather to baby Étienne who died so young.

He had lost his wife to the smallpox epidemic. Marie-Anne Perré had left behind two daughters. She had come from a wealthy merchant family and would have brought a large dowry to her husband. This may explain how Charles had managed to buy a substantial house on rue de l'Étang, in the same section of the town as rue Royalle.

The new ménage on rue de l'Étang consisted of Charles, his daughters, Marie (8) and Louise (6) and Marguerite, her son Abraham (10) and daughters Angélique (12) and Jeanne (5). Marguerite's older sons, Charles and Joseph, were living away. Now 23, Charles had established himself in Grand-Pré on land inherited from his father. Joseph fils (19) had been working with his father as a caboteur since the age of 15 and would continue on his own account, living in his late father's house on rue Royalle. He had inherited his father's schooner the *Marie-Josèphe*. When Charles visited Louisbourg he stayed with Joseph in the Dugas house.

Little Jeanne was very impressed with their new home on rue de l'Étang. It was a charpente house, timber-framed with a rubble stone infill, more substantial than the piquet house usually built by the Acadians. And it was larger and better furnished than the Dugas house on rue Royalle. Jeanne had wandered, wide-eyed, in the formal parlour when they had first arrived in their new home. It was very different from the usual Acadian home where the large kitchen was the general living quarters for the whole family. This house had a fashionably furnished parlour, with a beautiful tapestry on the wall, depicting elegantly gowned French shepherdesses. And there was a clavecin. The Acadians loved music and might have a violin and Jew's harp, but this was the first time Jeanne had seen a harpsichord. Angélique was enthralled with both the shepherdesses and the clavecin. She later told her little sister that she had that day sworn to herself that she would learn to play.

There were several bedrooms, and it was decided that Angélique would share a room with Marie and Louise, and Jeanne would share another with Abraham. This was unfortunate. It separated Jeanne from her sister and it meant that she was treated like a baby. At least that's the way she saw it.

Indeed she was very unsure of how she fit in the scheme of things in the new place. Not only was the house new and strange, Jeanne was no longer the centre of attention as the baby of the family, as she had been on rue Royalle. With

Charles and Joseph now away from the family circle, her step-father Monsieur de la Tour was the only man in her family.

To make matters worse, he seemed to be taking first place in Maman's attentions and affections. And of course Maman had two additional daughters to look after. Not that she neglected any of the children, but she often looked distracted. It was around this time that Jeanne developed her habit of quietly studying the people around her to see what she could expect of them.

Monsieur de la Tour, as the Dugas children called him, was a rather proud-looking man. No doubt kind – he was generous – but distant. Their father had been a down-to-earth, warm and rather noisy Acadian. Although as a caboteur he was often absent, when he was at home he was boister-ously affectionate with his children. Charles and Joseph fils, cut from the same cloth, had taken his place in Jeanne's life.

Jeanne watched Maman very carefully. She decided that although her mother seemed preoccupied, she looked happy. But it was not a happiness that reflected Jeanne's presence; the source lay somewhere else. Indeed, she seemed to be somehow a different person when Monsieur de la Tour was at home.

Maman changed in other ways too. Very soon a seam-stress came to stay with the new family while she made several beautiful new gowns in the French style. Maman said these were only for when she would accompany Monsieur de la Tour on special occasions. She continued to wear her Acadian clothes at home – at least until the new babies came. Oh yes, a year after the move, twin girls were born, Jeanne Charlotte and Anne.

There is no doubt that the new babies disrupted life on rue de l'Étang. Angélique, as the oldest girl, resented having to help look after them and Jeanne resented having to share Maman with them. Marie and Louise de la Tour no doubt now felt outnumbered by the Dugas, and the eleven-year-old Abraham overwhelmed by sisters. There had been a very real shift in all of their lives.

On the verge of young womanhood, Angélique seemed rather pleased with the new family's status. For, although Monsieur de la Tour insisted he was an Acadian, Angélique was old enough to see that he preferred to live in a manner more refined than most Acadians could aspire to.

Their new step-sisters, Marie and Louise, attended the convent of the Congrégation de Notre-Dame, a school for girls located near the de la Tour home. The only school in Louisbourg, it had been founded by Soeur de la Conception, a headstrong nun who had come to Louisbourg from Québec in 1727. The curriculum had a strong devotional basis, and behaviour and deportment were stressed. But the girls were also taught reading, writing and simple arithmetic, as well as needlework, music and crafts. The students were clearly meant to emerge as "proper young ladies." The convent accepted only daughters of the officers at the garrison, making rare exceptions for a few day students from deserving families like the de la Tours.

Angélique was hoping to go to the convent too, although at twelve she was at an age when most students would be finishing their schooling. There was another complication. The nuns were still looking after a number of girls who had been orphaned during the smallpox epidemic. But, when Monsieur de la Tour and Maman went to consult with the nuns, they agreed to accept Angélique as a day student. Because of her age she would receive instruction only in "young ladies' arts," that is, religion, deportment, needlework and music. Jeanne, to her great surprise – and concern – was told she had been accepted at the convent for the following year.

Angélique was pretty and had grand plans for her life. She began to plead with Maman for new French-style clothes. She could make them herself, she said. Monsieur de la Tour, amused at this girl-turning-young-woman, told Maman to have the seamstress come to make a couple of new gowns for her. Next, arrangements were made for Angélique to take dancing lessons from one of several dancing masters in Louisbourg. Jeanne was not sure if Maman really approved of this. She heard Maman scoff at Angélique's new airs one day. "Where do you think you're going to use your dancing skills?" she asked her daughter. But Angélique, obviously preoccupied with her new status in life, was practising languid poses in her new gowns, much to the amusement of Monsieur de la Tour.

All of this annoyed Jeanne, who was too old to be a baby and too young to be a young woman. She was secretly pleased to see that the de la Tour daughters, Marie and Louise, were also miffed by their father's treatment of Angélique. Maman sensed how Jeanne was feeling, and told her it would be her turn one day.

And so, the members of the new family settled in around each other, Maman at the centre of things and Monsieur de la Tour looming large in the background. As the eldest, Angélique held sway over Marie and Louise. Abraham kept to himself when he was at home and not out running around with friends. When she looked back, Jeanne could see that the twin baby girls had played a part in bringing the new family together. Even though at times resented by the other children, they were very sweet babies. And so Jeanne kept her careful watch on all the members of the new family.

—

Jeanne was worried about the idea of going to school. On her very first day she walked the short distance to the convent with her eyes down, nervously gripping Angélique's hand. She was scrubbed, polished and wore a new Acadian bonnet. Maman had wanted her to dress in the French style like Marie and Louise, but Jeanne had dug in her heels and refused, her first real act of defiance.

She arrived at the front door of the convent wearing a linen chemise with a dark-coloured vest over it, a striped linen skirt, a neck scarf, the new bonnet on her head and a determined look on her face. She was going to make the best of it.

As they arrived, Angélique whispered urgently, "Jeanne!" and tugged on her hand. Jeanne lifted her eyes just as the door opened and Mère Saint-Joseph appeared.

"Bonjour, ma jolie petite Acadienne!" she exclaimed. Jeanne's scowl disappeared and she smiled in spite of herself. That day she took to book-learning like a duck to water.

Chapter 4

In the mid-1730s there were rumblings of the threat of yet another war between France and Britain. It stood to reason that having taken over Acadia, the English would want to extend their reach to the neighbouring areas, and the growth and development of Louisbourg had begun to be perceived as a threat to British trade. By 1739 the rumours were becoming more persistent and there was a resulting decline in the cod fishery. Fishing entrepreneurs in Europe were reluctant to risk sending ships and men to an area that might be engaged in fighting another war. The rumours also affected trade, an important part of the port's economy.

While the cod-fishing industry was a large undertaking and the basis for the economy of Louisbourg and Île Royale, the town was also a very important trading centre. It had warehouses, careening wharf, admiralty court, harbour defences and the first lighthouse in the area. During the 1730s an average of 150 ships a year would sail into its harbour during the summer season, making Louisbourg one of the busiest ports in the new world.

Most of the huge profits made from the cod-fishing industry found their way into the coffers of the French king; then the traders and shippers benefited, followed by the fishermen. When the catch was abundant, Louisbourg was a prosperous place – even though life was very hard for the people who worked long hours at the seashore tending the flakes where the cod was dried. They were poorly paid for the very long hours of work. Whereas in Acadia the settlers who had farmland and farm animals prospered, Louisbourg had no farming to speak of and the poor often had no money to buy the foodstuffs that were, of necessity, imported.

The wealthy, however, lived very well. There was a social hierarchy, with the governor and the officers of the garrison at the top, followed by traders, navigators and craftsmen, then tavern keepers and shopkeepers. There were also musicians, dance instructors, seamstresses, laundresses and people who kept gaming establishments. Gaming was a pastime for all levels of society there.

If you ignored the dark clouds of impending war, Louisbourg was a busy, bustling community and an exciting place to live. These were the two realities: the busy, happy outer life and an inner life of worry and apprehension as to what the future would bring.

Chapter 5

If a bit more reserved and disciplined, life at the house on rue de l'Étang was even busier than it had been on rue Royalle. Monsieur de la Tour was absent for brief periods of time, but he had a full crew on his schooner and it often sailed without him.

Jeanne's brother Joseph was a frequent visitor to the de la Tour home when he was not at sea. Since taking command of his own ship at the age of fifteen he had been a supplier of firewood to the garrison at Louisbourg, and this business brought him a large income. In 1737, in partnership with two other men, he obtained a three-year charter to provide the garrison and civilians with fresh beef. There was some controversy over his having a monopoly for this service and the fact that the live cattle he delivered sometimes came from Nova Scotia, despite the policy that beef should not come from British colonies. Joseph was a very good trader, however, and somehow managed to overcome that obstacle.

Jeanne's brother Charles was established at Grand-Pré, on property he had inherited from his father. Perhaps not as aggressive a businessman as his brother, Charles was a farmer, a well-known shipbuilder and ran a smaller caboteur trade.

When he visited Île Royale several times a year, he stayed with Joseph in the house on rue Royalle, and the two brothers would visit with the de la Tour family. Monsieur de la Tour treated his two older stepsons as equals and they often discussed business and politics together.

Charles often tried to convince Joseph to settle with him in Grand-Pré, saying that the Acadians were once again prospering under English rule. But, like his father had been in 1714, Joseph was wary of the situation.

—

In the fall of 1739, Joseph's family and the de la Tours sailed to Grand-Pré, staying through the winter and spring of 1740, sharing Charles and Uncle Abraham's farmsteads.

Maman made sure that everyone was outfitted with Acadian dress for the trip. Angélique objected, but Monsieur de la Tour agreed with Maman on this matter, and insisted that Angélique was not to put on "airs."

Now almost sixteen years old, Angélique had finished her two years of schooling at the convent. She was beginning to find some success as a proper young lady in the Louisbourg's social life, although she was never likely to reach the upper circle that included the governor's mansion. Unless, of course, she married very well.

Angélique had a delicate prettiness, with a fair skin, blue-grey eyes, and light brown hair. She and her brothers Charles and Abraham favoured their mother, while Jeanne and Joseph favoured their father, with dark eyes and hair and a sturdier build.

Monsieur de la Tour also adopted Acadian dress for their voyage. Jeanne, after studying him quietly from a distance, decided that he looked less strict and distant in his Acadian clothes, and she told him that she liked him better that way.

He laughed and said, "Well, ma petite Jeanne, you would have liked my great-grandfather Charles de Saint-Étienne de la Tour.

"Tell me about him," she said.

"He sailed to Acadia with his father Claude on the ship *Grâce de Dieu* in 1610. They were coming here to go into the fur trade. My great-grandfather, who was only fourteen, and another boy his own age, Charles Biencourt, grew up among the Mi'kmaq. They spoke their language and learned to live in the native manner. They knew how to use birch bark canoes and snowshoes, to snare moose and spear salmon, and to dress in moccasins, with leggings of moose or seal skin, and topped with a cape of fur or a blanket.

"My great-grandfather married a Mi'kmaw princess and they had five children. And during all this time he took part in the fur trade and the politics it involved. But later on he realized that it would be better for him to have a wife with the right connections in France. He went to France and found one – her name was Françoise Jacquelin, and she became totally committed to him and his enterprise in Acadia."

Jeanne stared at him wide-eyed.

"Do you want to hear more?" he smiled.

"Yes. Oh yes."

Monsieur de la Tour went on to explain that his great-grandfather became involved in a struggle for power in Acadia with a man named Charles de Menou d'Aulnay. But when his wife Françoise died, and then d'Aulnay also died in a boating accident, his great-grandfather proposed to d'Aulnay's widow, Jeanne Morin de Reux. That put an end to the struggle between the two men.

"And most people agree, at least those on his side, that my great-grandfather was the first governor of Acadia."

"Ah, mon Dieu," Jeanne said.

"So you see, Jeanne, when I dress like this I think of my great-grandfather and I feel close to him. It's Acadian dress, not Mi'kmaw, but it feels closer to the land.

"And there's something else you should know. When the ship *Saint-Jehan* arrived here in 1636, bringing settlers to work the land, your own ancestor Abraham Dugas was among them. And he too became an important person in this new land."

"Thank you, Monsieur de la Tour. I must go and tell Joseph." And Jeanne ran off.

—

Living in Grand-Pré was an exciting time for the younger children, who had never been to Acadia nor lived on a farm. Abraham was thirteen, almost a man; Jeanne was nine; the de la Tour girls, Marie and Louise, were eleven and ten; the twins, Charlotte and Anne, were only two.

Even the weather was different in Acadia. Winters in Louisbourg were bone-chillingly grey, foggy and wet – spring and fall were much the same, some said. Although most of the streets were cobbled, in bad weather they collected debris and became slippery. Snow quickly became slush. In Grand-Pré, winter seemed to be different. The snow stayed clean and white on the farms and even though it was cold the sun shone and the fields sparkled. Acadian houses were snug and warm and well supplied with hearty food. The Dugas and de la Tour children got to know the farm animals and both children and adults enjoyed sleigh rides and walks in the snow. The new year was celebrated at Charles's home, with his new wife, Anne Leblanc.

Charles and Anne had married in January of 1739. Charles was over twenty-five and had not needed his mother's permission to marry. In his own quiet and independent manner, Charles had simply informed his mother and siblings of his marriage on his first trip to Île Royale that spring. He had not brought his bride with him to meet the family but he insisted that both he and Anne wanted them to visit Grand-Pré.

When she first met them Anne had mentioned that she had been a bit shy at the idea of meeting Monsieur de la Tour. Taking this all in, Jeanne exclaimed, "But he's only an Acadian like us!" Everyone laughed, including Monsieur de la Tour who had come into the room unnoticed.

—

Despite the general merriment and good cheer that the families enjoyed in Grand-Pré, the problems of Louisbourg were not left behind. Jeanne had heard the men talk about this around the supper table at rue de l'Étang. But she was surprised to hear the heated political discussion at Charles and Uncle Abraham's homes in Grand-Pré. She got in the habit of sitting quietly in the same room and listening when the men lingered around the supper table in the evening.

After a particularly loud and heated argument one evening, her brother Joseph noticed Jeanne listening to them. He walked over and knelt beside her chair.

"Jeanne, ma petite, wipe that frown off your face. There is nothing for you to worry about."

"But Joseph, you say that we might have to leave Louisbourg. And maybe even leave Grand-Pré. Where would we go? Would we all go together? To the same place? I am afraid."

Joseph put his arms around her. "No, Jeanne. No. Whatever happens we will all stay together. I promise. And nothing has happened yet. Probably nothing will. Now, don't worry. Go and play with the other children. You are too serious." He smiled at her. "Go on now."

She left the room, but could not make herself stop worrying. The next day, she put on her sternest face and asked Joseph to explain the situation to her. "Please just tell me," she said, stamping her foot. "Otherwise, I am going to worry. I may be only ten years old, or almost, but I am not stupid!"

"No, my little Jeanne, you are very smart. Get your warm clothes on and come to the barn with me. We can talk while I clean the stalls."

—

She sat on a bale of hay, her breath visible in the cold air of the barn, while Joseph worked and talked.

"Jeanne, do you learn any history at the convent?"

"Not very much. I don't think that interests the sisters. I know that France and Britain are enemies. And the sisters seem to think that le bon Dieu is on the side of the French. But I find that hard to understand. The sisters don't seem to care much what happens to the Acadians or the Mi'kmaq," she sighed.

"But I do like to go to school. I like the reading, writing and arithmetic, but the young ladies' arts don't seem very important to me. I can sew, but I have real trouble with the embroidery. Mère Saint-Joseph said she would help me next year. I have to embroider a 'beautiful shawl,'" she said, rolling her eyes.

Joseph laughed. "Jeanne, you are very lucky to be going to school. It's not everyone who can go. And even the young ladies' arts will be helpful to you in the future."

Jeanne just shrugged. "I don't just worry about us, Joseph. I worry about all the Acadians. We are real Acadians, aren't we?"

"Yes, Jeanne, we are real Acadians. And proud of it. As Monsieur de la Tour told you, our ancestor Abraham Dugas sailed to the new world a hundred years ago."

"Another Abraham," said Jeanne.

"Yes," Joseph said with a laugh. "That's why we have so many Abrahams in our family. They were all named after him. This first Abraham was born in France, where he had the title of Armourer of the King, a gunsmith. Here in Acadia, he had the title of Lieutenant General. He was one of the three most important men in the new colony. He had a large farm, but he was also an armourer, a justice of the peace and chief of police. He married a woman named Marguerite Doucet and they had eight children. Our father was his grandson. So you are his great-granddaughter."

Jeanne was captivated with the story and sat quietly, trying to commit it to memory.

"Our forefathers worked hard," Joseph said, "but they made an honest living. They owned land, something that was impossible for ordinary people in France. They had full bellies and a roof over their heads. Some of them became wealthy."

"But, Joseph, this took a long time, didn't it?"

"More than a hundred years. And during this time the new colony changed hands many times between France and Britain. For a long time the Acadians were able to continue to live on their prosperous farms even under British rule. But when Acadia fell again to the British in 1710, many Acadians believed that this was the end. Many were afraid for their survival."

"Now Acadia is called Nova Scotia," Jeanne said. "But we still think of it as Acadia, don't we?"

"Yes, Jeanne, we do."

Joseph paced back and forth as he cleaned the stalls, stopping now and then to speak directly to Jeanne when he wanted to make sure she was following his story.

"Our father, Joseph, was one of the young men who worried about the political situation. He left Grand-Pré to go to Île Royale and he settled in Port Toulouse. Charles and I were

33

just babies, so I don't remember much about our first years there. But I know that Maman was very glad to leave that place to go to live at Louisbourg about ten years later.

"Jeanne, you know that we had three little sisters who were born in Port Toulouse? And that they died in Louisbourg during the smallpox epidemic, when you were just a baby?"

Jeanne nodded. "I know. Marie Madeleine, Marguerite and Anne. Maman always says their names in her prayers. And there was Étienne who was born and died in Louisbourg."

"Yes." He paused.

"So now there is again the possibility of war between France and Britain. That's what all the talk is about. I think it's good that you know and understand this, Jeanne, but I don't want you to worry. We will be safe. Monsieur de la Tour has good contacts at the garrison and he will know if our situation becomes dangerous. We will get away in time."

"Thank you for telling me, Joseph." Then with a serious and piercing look, Jeanne asked if he was named Joseph because he was the one most like their father.

"I'm not sure," Joseph smiled. "Maybe. They say I look like him."

"I like Monsieur de la Tour," Jeanne said, "but I don't think of him as my father."

"That's all right, Jeanne. I know he likes you."

"No, I think he likes Angélique better, because she is very pretty."

"Oh, Jeanne. You are pretty too. Angélique is pretty, but she's not smart like you." He paused. "If there are difficult times ahead, you'll be fine. Angélique – well, I don't know. If she saw an enemy army advancing, she'd probably try to flirt with the officers. But then, maybe this would be smart. I'm not being serious, Jeanne, I didn't mean that."

He smiled. "Come on, you'd best be getting back to the house. I don't want to have to explain to Maman why I let you freeze on a haystack."

Jeanne jumped up and went to him for a hug. "Will you let me know what is happening, Joseph?"

"Yes, I promise. Run along now."

———

Early in the new year, Joseph surprised everyone with the news that he had asked Anne's cousin, Marguerite Leblanc, to marry him. They had decided they should marry in Grand-Pré while the whole family was there.

"We are grateful to have all of you here for a visit," smiled Marguerite, blushing. "Otherwise he might never have had the nerve to ask!"

Marguerite was the daughter of Joseph Leblanc dit Le Maigre (the skinny one), so-called because he was very fat. Like Joseph Dugas, he was a caboteur, and a very successful one. It was said that at one time he was the wealthiest man in Acadia.

The wedding was celebrated just before Lent. There was much merrymaking and music to accompany the happy event, and the de la Tour family met more members of the Dugas extended family and other Acadians from the surrounding farms. Jeanne saw only happy faces when she looked around at her family and relatives gathered together. Grand-Pré was obviously a wonderful place. She wondered why everyone was so worried about the fate of the people who were living here.

When they returned to Louisbourg in the spring, Joseph brought his bride home to set up housekeeping with him on rue Royalle. The following year, their first child, Marguerite Dugas, was born.

Chapter 6

L ouisbourg was bustling with activity when the de la Tour family and Joseph and Marguerite returned, although fewer ships than usual had arrived. An eagerly awaited commodity carried by the first ships of the season was always the news, especially political news, but in the spring of 1740 there was nothing decisive to report. France and Britain had avoided going to war with each other in 1739, but what did the future hold?

—

Although the uncertain fate of Louisbourg cast a shadow, life in the de la Tour home continued at a busy pace. The family had enjoyed their stay in Grand-Pré, but they all slipped back happily into their life in the big town – especially Maman and Angélique. Jeanne, now more aware of the situation thanks to her brother Joseph, continued to watch those around her for signs and omens.

Almost immediately, Joseph sailed away on one of his schooners, and the family helped Marguerite to settle into the house on rue Royalle. After having watched her carefully for some time, Jeanne decided she approved of Joseph's wife, a kind, gentle woman, and she began to spend time with her at the house on rue Royalle.

Marie, Louise and Jeanne returned to their lessons at the convent (Angélique was now too old) and Jeanne continued to work on her embroidered shawl. She tackled it with the same grim determination she applied to all unpleasant tasks. Mère Saint-Joseph, suppressing a smile, told her that her work was much improved and gave her one of the coveted ginger biscuits that were kept in a big tin box at the convent.

In 1742 and 1743, Marie and Louise, one after the other, finished their schooling at the convent and joined Angélique among the ranks of proper young ladies in Louisbourg's social scene. Of course this created a flurry of excited preparations, with new gowns, parties, agonizing over invitations, and participation as young adults in the yearly celebrations held for the Feast of Sainte-Anne in July and the Feast of Saint-Louis in August.

The family members looked very handsome in their fine French clothes when they walked into the Chapelle Saint-Louis at the garrison on special occasions. But Jeanne insisted on wearing her Acadian dress even though she did at times feel rather silly doing so. She told herself that she did this to show sympathy for the poorly dressed ordinary people, many of them Acadians, standing at the back of the Chapelle. But what difference did her gesture make? Being Acadian did not necessarily mean being poor; the Dugas and the de la Tour families were proof of that. Angélique, who was furious with Jeanne for doing this, accused her of being stubborn and contrary, which only made Jeanne dig her heels in more. It also made her a bit sad because it distanced her from her sister and step-sisters. Maman understood, but said that Jeanne was only making life difficult for herself.

On the whole Jeanne was not unhappy. She liked going to school at the convent. She thrived on and excelled at learning. She tolerated the religious lessons and etiquette classes well enough and would have enjoyed the crafts and sewing classes if not for the dreaded shawl. But she finished it, and before she left the convent Mère Saint-Joseph herself embroidered in one corner of the shawl the likeness of a small and beautiful Acadian bonnet. She embroidered her initials, MSJ, below. Jeanne would keep the shawl with her all her life, through all her travels and trials, as one of her most treasured possessions.

Joseph encouraged her to study. His own reading skills were skimpy. When he started to bring her documents and contracts to read for him, she saw the value of her schooling. When she complained that the convent had only religious books to read, Joseph went to Jacques Rolland's boutique and bought a selection for her from the bibliothèque bleu series. These were booklets in soft blue covers, with folk tales, contes de mère l'oye and fantastical stories of myths and legends, as well as some pastorelles, stories in verse on pastoral themes. Jeanne was ecstatic.

—

While the first ships to arrive at Louisbourg in the spring were the most important source for direct news, the officers at the garrison seemed to know best what the consequences of such news might be. There were other sources, such as the many taverns in Louisbourg, where military men, merchants and sailors spent their idle hours. Some taverns catered to the ordinary people and others had a higher class of clients. Even the many boutiques, where imported luxury fabrics and fashionable accessories were sold, were good places to pick up gossip and rumour.

Monsieur de la Tour was well placed to take advantage of all these sources of information, and many discussions took place in the de la Tour home. Jeanne did her best to listen in, even if she did not always understand. Whenever Joseph caught her with a frown on her face, he would rub his finger on the crease and say, "Jeanne, what did I tell you about not worrying?" He kept his promise to keep her informed, although she sometimes wondered if he told her everything.

—

In the spring of 1742, the Colony learned that France and England were once again at war, each allied with opposing sides in a European conflict over who would succeed to the throne of the Hapsburg dynasty. The question on everyone's mind was whether this would lead to direct conflict between the two old enemies, which would almost certainly mean war in the colonies.

Early that summer, the de la Tours and Joseph and his family again visited Grand-Pré, and stayed for a month. The mood during this visit seemed more sombre than the last time. Again there were discussions around the supper table, but Jeanne was not always allowed to listen in. On this matter, Joseph was very stern with her. "I will tell you what is going on, Jeanne," he said. "I promise."

Jeanne realized later that they must have been making plans in case the rumours of war became true. When they returned to Louisbourg, Angélique chose to stay behind in peaceful Grand-Pré with their elder brother Charles and his family.

—

An atmosphere of tension and unease still hung over Louisbourg. Rumours of war persisted, and the possibility of new hostilities kept many fishermen from risking a trip across the ocean, which only worsened the situation. Spring food shortages were a normal part of life here because of Louisbourg's dependence on imported food. Normally the hundreds of Basque fishing vessels would bring extra food supplies with them on their first voyage of the season, but the sharp decrease in traffic meant an accompanying decrease in much-needed food supplies. Of course it was the poor who suffered the most. Many faced starvation in the spring of 1743 and again in 1744.

Furthermore, the summer of 1743 was one of the worst seasons for the fishermen of Île Royale. There was a sense of gloom as the Feast of Saint-Michel approached in the fall. This celebration coincided with the end of the fishing season and it was the day when cod stocks were measured and compared with the fishermen's debts. In fact, the day had become the deadline for all kinds of accounts, not just for that of the fishermen. The feast marked an end to another difficult year in Louisbourg.

That same year also brought the sad news of Angélique's death in Grand-Pré. Joseph had the task of telling the family when he returned from his first voyage there in the spring. She had caught a fever that could not be treated and died in her brother Charles's home after only a brief illness. She was eighteen. It was a shock to all the family and Jeanne felt especially sad, because she thought she might have been unkind to Angélique.

When Joseph and Marguerite's second daughter was born a few months later, they named her Anne Angélique.

Chapter 7

B ad news arrived on May 3, 1744, on board a ship from Saint-Malo that carried the official dispatches of the Ministre de la Marine. A letter signed by le Ministre, the Comte de Maurepas, announced that France had declared war on Britain. It was not a surprise, but it was not welcome news. This would be the first time that Louisbourg would be caught in the crossfire.

It was difficult enough governing the colony of Île Royale during peaceful years. The declaration of war could make things intolerable, though some junior officers at the garrison no doubt looked forward to the opportunities that war would bring, and some merchants looked forward to making extra profits outfitting privateers. For the poor who were dependent on the fishery, however, war meant reduced catches and the danger of being captured at sea by enemy ships.

The officials at the garrison were faced with many difficult decisions – the most urgent was the food shortage. They organized a successful raid against the small British fort at Canceau at the eastern tip of mainland Nova Scotia. The fort was looted and destroyed, several British vessels taken, and more than 100 men taken prisoner. This bold move robbed the British of their shore base and freed the sea-lanes for vessels bringing supplies to Île Royale. And it gave the inhabitants of Louisbourg a victory to celebrate.

The next step was to arrange for French privateers to attack British commerce in the vicinity of Île Royale. In times of war, privateering provided ships and manpower for the king, and was a lucrative, if dangerous, occupation for its practitioners. They were authorized to capture and loot enemy vessels, whether military, commercial or fishery, and to take their crews as prisoners. Later they would be asked to give an accounting of their activities to the authorities and to forfeit a portion of their loot to the king.

In the month of June, French privateers still had the element of surprise on their side, as news of the declaration of war was slow to arrive among the British colonies. By the end of the month, about a dozen British ships and their cargoes had been captured and many others driven away from the nearby waters. The confiscated cargoes brought desperately needed supplies.

By mid-summer, the French privateers faced the prospect of conducting their raids farther south in the busier shipping lanes to and from Boston. There was potential for greater profits, but a greater potential for danger. At the same time, a schooner was hired to serve as a coast guard vessel to patrol the waters around Louisbourg to protect their fishing interests. The officials at the garrison also sent supplies to Port Toulouse and Port Dauphin, and nurtured their alliance with the Mi'kmaq.

—

The young colonial lieutenant in charge of Canceau at the time was one Jean-Baptiste Bradstreet – John, as he became known. He was taken prisoner, but because he was an officer, was related to the de la Tour family and had connections at Louisbourg, he was free to roam the fortress.

Chapter 8

The coming and going of the many ships and boats that anchored at the port the summer of 1744 brought an element of excitement to the inhabitants of Louisbourg. The vessels visiting the port had always been the source for news, but the war now created greater urgency for their reports. The most sought-after news concerned the activities of the Louisbourg privateers and the movements of the enemy. Of course, rumours abounded, and it was part of the game to try to separate rumour from fact.

—

Conversation in Jeanne's home reflected the tensions fuelled by war. Monsieur de la Tour argued bitterly that decisions would be made on the other side of the ocean by two governing bodies that saw Île Royale as only a bargaining tool in their larger plans, with no thought for the livelihood of the people who lived and worked here. Joseph believed that the Acadians and the French settlers on Île Royale should fight for their rights. Eventually even Jeanne got tired of hearing the same old arguments.

It seemed to her that Joseph at times looked envious when there were reports of successful raids carried out by the privateers. Monsieur de la Tour too seemed to relish stories of these successes. Jeanne heard Joseph mutter under his breath one day, "Well, why don't you get one of your boats equipped and go out and try your luck?"

Joseph continued to carry freight and cattle from Île Saint-Jean and Nova Scotia to Louisbourg, with a token number of cattle from New France to fulfill the terms of his contract. One day when she was visiting Joseph's home on rue Royalle, Jeanne asked him about all this.

"Well, Jeanne, it's true that the privateers make big profits, but they take great risks too. I'm lucky to have the contracts that I have and I'm making good money. I don't need to be involved in a war."

Joseph's wife, Marguerite, gave him an anxious look. "Please don't even think of it," she said. "There's enough danger in what you're doing now." They both knew that Marguerite's father, Joseph Leblanc dit Le Maigre, was very much involved in privateering.

Jeanne looked from one to the other. "What is going to happen, Joseph?"

"No one knows, Jeanne. No one knows. And no one wins when there is a war. No one. But a lot of people will take advantage of it."

"If Louisbourg falls, will we still be Acadian, Joseph?"

"Jeanne," Joseph smiled. "You have your stubborn face on again. Are you still worried about being Acadian? Remember what I told you? We will go back to Acadia."

What Joseph did not tell her then and what she would learn only after the end of the war, was that he was in fact involved in the war effort. Because his shipping activities allowed him to move freely between Île Royale and Nova Scotia, and because of his contacts with Mi'kmaw scouts, he was able to supply military intelligence to the French.

—

Jeanne's coming of age celebration that summer would be engraved in her memory as the first real turning point in her life. Many more would follow, forced on her by events beyond her control. She would live in the world of the fancy blue silk gown for a while longer, but not in the same carefree atmosphere as her sisters had.

Chapter 9

War stories circulated in the town. By the end of July, there were reports of many more British and New England privateers sailing closer to Île Royale, and the course of the war at sea was shifting. The arrival of privateers, with their prizes, prisoners and tales of high adventure, were eagerly awaited, but the early successes of the French privateers in June and July could not be maintained.

An exciting diversion occurred when six huge merchant ships owned by the Companie des Indes sailed into the harbour. The Companie had a monopoly over France's trade with the Far East. The ships were on their way from India back to France, and they had been told to proceed to Louisbourg because of the war. The ships brought hundreds of sailors and an air of excitement with them, distracting the people of Louisbourg from the worries of war for a brief moment. The event was discussed at length at the de la Tour home. But the worries of war remained.

In August, British privateers and warships were seen off the coast of Île Royale. They disrupted the French shipping lanes and in early August five French ships were captured.

—

The atmosphere at the de la Tour home was becoming more sombre. Joseph visited often and his discussions with Monsieur de la Tour sometimes became heated arguments. Monsieur de la Tour wanted the family to leave Île Royale in the fall before winter set in, but Joseph was very reluctant to go. They also could not agree on where to take refuge. Monsieur de la Tour wanted to go to Grand-Pré where they had family and property. Joseph preferred Île Saint-Jean, which was more convenient for his cabotage activities and closer to Île Royale should the war turn in their favour.

Monsieur de la Tour accused Joseph of being a dreamer if he believed that the war would turn in their favour. In turn Joseph thought de la Tour was the dreamer, if he thought they would find a safe and permanent refuge in Grand-Pré under British rule.

"If Louisbourg falls, then we lose the French colony and that means both Île Royale and Île Saint-Jean," Joseph said. "Do you think the British will want to keep the Acadians around then? It's only your generation that believes the Acadians can go on living here indefinitely."

Monsieur de la Tour paused and seemed to be considering his next comments very seriously.

"Joseph, I'm as much an Acadian as you are, or Jeanne," he said smiling at her, "but I think we are looking at simple survival here, unless we want to be deported to France when Louisbourg falls. And I think none of us wants this."

Joseph grimaced and hung his head.

"I may be getting old," Monsieur de la Tour continued, but we have to think of our families. We have plans to go to Grand-Pré and I believe that is our safest option now. Joseph, are you being influenced by your father-in-law? He seems to me to be a rash man. This is no time for that."

The two men's wives exchanged a worried look. Joseph's wife said to him, "You know I love my Papa, but I trust Monsieur de la Tour's judgement in this."

In the end, Monsieur de la Tour's views prevailed and the two families made plans to leave for Grand-Pré by the end of September. It was agreed that they would make their preparations quietly and not draw unnecessary attention to their departure.

One day Joseph found Jeanne trying to decide what to pack for their voyage, the familiar frown on her face. "Jeanne," he asked, "what's troubling you?"

"Oh, Joseph, should I bring my blue silk gown with me? I haven't had much chance to wear it and I don't know if I'll be able to wear it over there."

"I know," he said, "and I'm sorry. Take it with you, but don't pack it yet. You'll be able to wear it for the feast day of Saint-Louis."

But the feast day of Saint-Louis, on August 25, normally Louisbourg's largest public celebration, was cut back that year. The huge bonfire and military salutes were cancelled. Jeanne wore her gown, but the festivities were very subdued, especially for the de la Tours and the Dugas, whose planned departure lay heavy on their hearts.

———

The officials at the garrison were very worried. The biggest problem was a serious food shortage, caused mainly by British ships intercepting French supply vessels off their coast. Louisbourg was facing a British blockade of its port and winter was approaching.

In September, two heavily armed French warships, the *Ardent* and the *Caribou*, arrived off the coast of Île Royale.

They drove away enemy ships, and some Louisbourg privateers and warships regained access to British waters. However, *Ardent* and *Caribou* were to return to France before winter and there was no assurance that they would come back in the spring.

A few weeks before the families left Île Royale, Jeanne's favourite nun, Mère Saint-Joseph, also sailed away. She had been the superior of the Congrégation de Notre-Dame since 1733. On the day of her departure, Joseph took Jeanne to the quay to say farewell to her. Jeanne told her that she would soon be leaving too and started to weep.

"Jeanne," Mère Saint-Joseph told her, "you are strong and you must be brave too. I have faith in you and I will pray for you. Are you taking your beautiful shawl with you?"

"Yes, of course," Jeanne smiled through her tears. "I'll keep it with me always."

—

The de la Tour and Dugas families left for Grand-Pré in September. On the last day of November, following the worst year in the history of the cod fishery, fifty ships set sail from Louisbourg for France, leaving only a few vessels tied up in the harbour for the winter. Many men who would normally have spent the winter in the colony chose to leave with the ships because of the uncertainty over war.

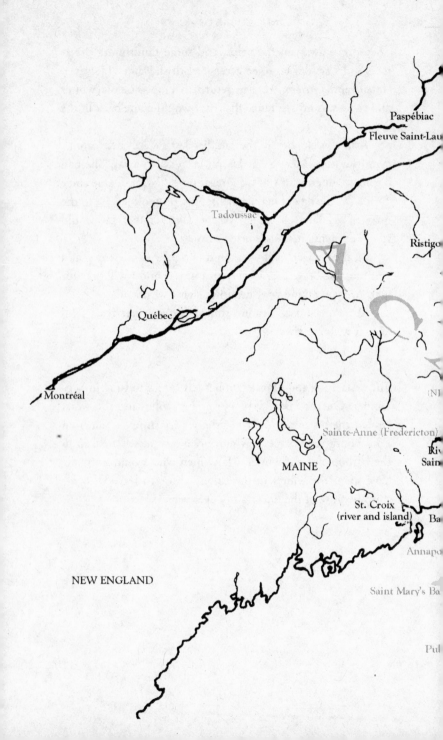

Paspébiac

Fleuve Saint-Lau

Tadoussac

Ristigo

Québec

Montréal

(N[

Sainte-Anne (Fredericton)

Riv
Sain

MAINE

St. Croix
(river and island)

Ba

Annapo

NEW ENGLAND

Saint Mary's Ba

Pu[

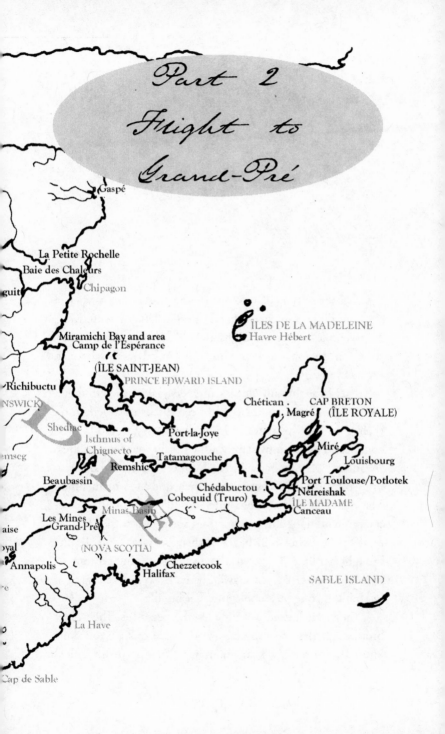

Part 2

Flight to

Grand-Pré

Gaspé

La Petite Rochelle

Baie des Chaleurs

guit

Chipagon

ÎLES DE LA MADELEINE
Havre Hébert

Miramichi Bay and area
Camp de l'Espérance

"
(ÎLE SAINT-JEAN)
PRINCE EDWARD ISLAND

Richibuctu

NSWICK

Chétican .

CAP BRETON
Magré (ÎLE ROYALE)

Shediac

Isthmus of
Chignecto

mseg

Port-la-Joye

Tatamagouche

Remshic

Miré

Louisbourg

Beaubassin

Chédabuctou .
Cobequid (Truro)

Port Toulouse/Potlotek
Neireishak
ÎLE MADAME
Canceau

Minas Basin

Les Mines
Grand-Pré

aise

oyal

(NOVA SCOTIA)

Annapolis

Chezzetcook
Halifax

SABLE ISLAND

e

o

La Have

Cap de Sable

Chapter 10

After the settling of accounts on the Feast of Saint-Michel, the de la Tour and Dugas families left for Grand-Pré. Monsieur de la Tour and his household sailed on his schooner, the *Cygne*. Joseph Dugas and his family sailed on his schooner, the *Marie-Josèphe*.

They brought only clothes and personal items with them. Their removal to Grand-Pré had been discussed at length on their previous trips there and they knew they would be welcomed and taken in by family. Once again they were to dress "Acadian." Maman had allowed Jeanne, Marie and Louise to bring only one French-style gown each, and a few mementoes. Marie and Louise brought souvenirs of their life in Louisbourg, invitations and favours from social events they had attended; the twins each brought their favourite doll. Jeanne brought her blue silk gown, the necklace and her portrait, as well as her embroidered shawl. She had also sneaked most of her bibliothèque bleu books into her bundle.

They were indeed welcomed with open arms. Their older brother Charles was especially glad to see them. "You don't know the stories we hear about what's going on in Louisbourg," he said. "And Joseph, my brother, you're here too. You're here."

"Yes, well, I am here à contre-gré, but very happy to see you for all that, Charles. I don't know how our relatives here are going to cope with all of us."

"Well, don't worry," Charles said. "The only problem we've had is fighting over who will have you stay with them. And the harvest has been very good this year. It will be our joy to share it with you. Let me see your girls, Joseph."

"Here they are," said Joseph. "Marguerite and Anne Angélique – named for our sister." Joseph handed his one-year-old to Charles.

"Yes. Bonjour, little Anne Angélique. You know, Joseph, I think she will look just like our Angélique." Charles had four children himself, the last just a baby. The other three were crowded around to see the new arrivals.

The following day, Charles took the de la Tour family and Joseph to the Saint-Charles-des-Mines cemetery to visit Angélique's gravesite. Jeanne stood beside Maman, holding her hand. When Maman's prayers were interrupted by tears, Jeanne continued for her. At the end she added Maman's plea that God bless Marie Madeleine, Marguerite and Anne, and little baby Étienne. Maman squeezed Jeanne's hand in thanks.

Charles, who had talked to them of Angélique's last days, told Maman again how sorry he was that he had not been able to prevent her death.

"Charles, my son, I know you did all you could. We have to accept that these things are in the hands of le bon Dieu," said Maman. "As perhaps we now have to accept that we are in His hands in our present situation."

No one argued with her.

—

Maman, Monsieur de la Tour, Louise, Marie and the twins stayed with Charles and his family. Joseph, his family, Jeanne and young Abraham were lodged with Uncle Abraham.

Jeanne withdrew into herself at first, having to adjust not only to being away from home, but also to living with her brother Joseph and his family rather than with Maman. It's not that she objected to the arrangement – she was fond of both Joseph and his wife – but it was a kind of second separation for Jeanne. She redoubled her careful scrutiny of those around her and of her surroundings. When she realized that Monsieur de la Tour and Charles would be coming to Uncle Abraham's farm for the usual around-the-table discussions on their plight, she was grateful that she would be there. Their first serious discussion had taken place following the family's visit to Angélique's gravesite.

Uncle Abraham had in the past been one of the delegates chosen to represent the Acadians of the Grand-Pré area to the British authorities and he held very firm views on the politics of the day. He had heard of Louisbourg's successful raid against the British fort at Canceau in early summer and of the French privateers' success in capturing British ships.

Now Joseph confirmed for him that the tide had turned and that the British, helped by forces from their colonies, had inflicted losses on Louisbourg and seriously disrupted their supply routes and the activities of their privateers. "There is grave concern at the garrison that the British may be able to blockade the port next summer," Joseph added, "unless the French government sends us some warships early in the spring."

"What can you tell me about this man, Duvivier?" Uncle Abraham asked. "I understand he's in charge of organizing a raid on Annapolis Royal, but I'm afraid he's going to do us harm here in Acadia."

It was Monsieur de la Tour who replied.

"I'm not proud of it, but he's one of my cousins. François du Pont Duvivier is also a great-grandson of Charles de Saint-Étienne de la Tour, on his mother's side. He joined the regular colonial troops when he was very young, and in his mid-twenties he was appointed an adjutant at Louisbourg, at about the same time as his uncle Louis du Pont Duchambon became Louisbourg's commander. So Duvivier has the protection of the garrison. And he has thrown himself into business, doing a lot of trading in Île Royale and Acadia, as well as in France and the West Indies. He has a finger in a lot of pies. And he has the protection of the two commercial officials at Louisbourg. He's made himself a fortune." Monsieur de la Tour turned to Joseph.

"You know something about this, Joseph. When Le Normant set up a monopoly to supply fresh meat to Louisbourg, it was generally believed that while you got the contract, it was controlled by Duvivier."

"You know very well this was never proven," replied Joseph. "And I don't care to discuss it now." Everyone fell silent. Jeanne was in a corner of the room, trying to remain unnoticed and take everything in. Joseph broke the silence.

"You must give Duvivier his due. He led the attack on Canceau and he brought more than one hundred prisoners back to Louisbourg."

Uncle Abraham snorted. "Yes, and who was the young colonial lieutenant in charge of the fort who was taken as one of the prisoners?" He stared at Monsieur de la Tour.

Monsieur de la Tour shifted a little in his chair and sighed. "Another one of my cousins, John Bradstreet – Jean-Baptiste."

"When he came to Louisbourg as a prisoner this summer, he was given preferential treatment," Monsieur de la Tour continued. "I stayed away from him, but I did see him wandering around Louisbourg. I confess it made me feel uneasy."

Uncle Abraham snorted again. "I don't know," he said, "whether we should ask God to protect us from the British, or from our cousins." There was nervous laughter around the table.

"To get back to Duvivier," said Monsieur de la Tour. "I've heard that he is organizing a raid against Annapolis Royal. It's meant to be a follow-up to the raid on Canceau, and the start of a movement to regain Acadia. Duvivier expects to receive some ships and men from France. I understand he has recruited some Mi'kmaq and some Malecite from the rivière Saint-Jean area, and he hopes to recruit some Acadians here.

"I must admit," Monsieur de la Tour continued, "that I'm not convinced of Duvivier's abilities. Canceau was his first military venture and it was a very easy victory. That fort was small and totally unprepared for an attack. How he will manage at Annapolis, I don't know."

Uncle Abraham interjected. "And then this fool Joseph Leblanc dit Le Maigre, all three hundred pounds of him, was going around as an advance party before Duvivier's tour, trying to encourage people to join the raiding party. I understand he did not have much success. I'm sorry, Joseph, I realize the man is your father-in-law."

"That's all right, Uncle. But my father-in-law is a very patriotic Acadian. Duvivier is his nephew. They only want to help the Acadian cause."

"Heaven help us – another relation! No, Joseph, they're not going to help the Acadian cause. They're going to help the French cause. And in doing that they're going to hurt the Acadian cause."

"What do you mean, Uncle?"

"They are not helping the Acadian cause," his uncle shouted. "I'll give you an example. Do you remember Alexandre Bourg dit Belle-Humeur? He was a notary here in Grand-Pré and a well-respected man. He was one of the Acadian delegates reporting to the British at Annapolis Royal. Well, he lost his post this year when the British accused him of collaborating with the French through his contacts with Le Maigre and his nephew Duvivier. I doubt very much that he did collaborate, but it makes no difference.

"There's something that the French, and you apparently, do not understand. We Acadians in Nova Scotia have become our own people. We have worked hard to create a place for ourselves here and we have found a way to live peaceably with the British authorities. We have not only survived, we have prospered.

"You know that very well, Joseph, you have carried Acadian goods to Louisbourg and Île Saint-Jean. And we are still on good terms with the Mi'kmaq."

"Yes, Uncle, but what about the Mi'kmaq?"

Uncle Abraham hesitated, then said, "Perhaps the most important thing we French did was to befriend the Mi'kmaq, or rather to let them befriend us. Our forefathers would have perished here without their help, and we have lived with them in peace. We farmed the lowlands; the Mi'kmaq continued to fish and to hunt in the forests. The British, I am sure, will want to take over the land completely as soon as they can bring their own people to settle here. I don't trust them."

"Ah, Uncle, you and Monsieur de la Tour are the older generation," Joseph said. "You don't have the mettle to do battle, do you?"

"We are the voice of experience," Uncle Abraham replied firmly. Joseph put his arm around his uncle's shoulder, to show he did not resent his views, but it was clear that Joseph did not agree with him.

"Do you know how the Duvivier campaign is going?" Monsieur de la Tour asked Uncle Abraham.

"No. It's supposed to be still going on now. One thing we do know is that the reinforcements Duvivier was expecting from France have not yet arrived and it does not look as if they will. I don't know what it means for us if the raid is successful. Either way, there will be more fighting and hardship."

Within a few days, there were reports that Duvivier's raid on Annapolis had indeed failed.

During the winter the British authorities interrogated the Acadian delegates in Grand-Pré about their actions during the expedition. The delegates insisted that the inhabitants of Grand-Pré had not given Duvivier any assistance except under duress. When asked about cattle conveyed to Louisbourg, the delegates replied that two droves of black cattle and sheep from Minas had been herded by Joseph Leblanc dit Le Maigre and Joseph Dugas. There were no immediate repercussions, but the people of Grand-Pré knew that this would not help their relations with the British authorities.

—

There was nothing for the families to do but to settle into the farm life of Grand-Pré for the winter months. After that first serious discussion, when Uncle Abraham made his views so clear, the men of the family met at least every other day. Joseph was not always there. He continued his cabotage activities as late into the fall as he could. And he brought back news, several times from Louisbourg itself. He managed to sail there at least twice before the sailing season ended. Sometimes he had news from other sea captains, sometimes from the Mi'kmaq. Joseph knew the three Mi'kmaw scouts, Jean Sauvage, Denis Michaud and François Muize, hired by the French to advise on the movements of British ships and their military. He kept in close contact with them.

It was Joseph's wife, Marguerite, who told Jeanne that Joseph had also been gathering military information for the French. She worried about her husband's safety.

"At least," she said, "I thank God that he did not get it into his head to become a privateer. I worry about my father too," she added, "but I know he's not going to change."

Not for the first time, Jeanne wondered how such a big, rough, rowdy man like Le Maigre could have such a gentle daughter as Marguerite.

Chapter 11

The officials at Louisbourg knew they would be facing war in the spring and summer of 1745, but they expected the attack to be led by British warships that would sail from England in the spring. They hoped that French warships would have arrived by then as well, but an early siege came from the New England colonies, led by William Pepperrell from the Colony of Massachusetts. The ships from New England first landed at Canceau, where they rebuilt the colonial fort's defences as they waited for the drift ice around Louisbourg to melt, where a group of small colonial warships was already blockading the fortress. In early May the siege began.

Louisbourg's fortifications were in a state of disrepair, and the garrison troops were insufficient in number and no doubt low in spirits. They fought nevertheless, unaware that the New Englanders had also moved artillery on land to attack from the rear.

A French man-of-war arrived at the end of May, bringing men and badly needed supplies, but after a fierce battle the ship was captured by the New England ships. Early in June the British fleet was at the harbour entrance. The combined land and sea attack, supported by the blockade of the harbour, lasted for almost seven weeks.

On June 26, 1745, the French initiated surrender. Under its terms, the military garrison were permitted to march out with the honours of war and the inhabitants were to be repatriated to France.

——

When the British and their colonial forces took possession of Louisbourg, Lieutenant John (Jean-Baptiste) Bradstreet was one of the first to make a grand entry. On his release from his imprisonment in Louisbourg the previous year, he had agreed not to bear arms against the French for a specific period of time. Given the freedom to roam about the fortress, Bradstreet had realized that it was vulnerable to attack by land from the rear. He broke his promise to the French and passed this intelligence on to Governor Shirley of the colony of Massachusetts, who used it effectively.

Lieutenant Bradstreet was rewarded with a promotion to the rank of Captain.

Chapter 12

Despite the fact that the Dugas men had known in their hearts and minds that it was inevitable, the news of Louisbourg's defeat came as a shock in Grand-Pré. Jeanne was surprised at their reaction. Uncle Abraham and her brothers Charles and Abraham accepted it. Joseph was angry and bitter.

"The maudit French couldn't even send a proper warship that could fight!" he said.

"I told you so!" Monsieur de la Tour responded.

Joseph was continuing his cabotage activities as much as possible and he was away for periods of time. Jeanne was more aware of Joseph's business dealings than other members of the family because she read his contracts for him. She also knew that his father-in-law was involved in some of her brother's activities, and, like her sister-in-law Marguerite, hoped Le Maigre would not get Joseph involved in anything to do with the war.

Again, Jeanne saw a shift, a kind of realignment, in the family. Although there was relief that they had left Louisbourg in time and would not be facing deportation to France, they now had to make some difficult decisions. Could they stay in

Grand-Pré? If not, where would they go? What choices did they have?

Charles, the eldest, assumed that they would all stay in Grand-Pré. "After all," he said, "there is land here that belonged to our father and that you, Joseph and Abraham, can start farming for yourselves. You can do well."

"Jeanne," he added with a smile, "you can marry a nice Acadian boy here and then you will truly be Acadienne." Jeanne's fierce desire to be Acadian when she was little had long since become a family joke.

Abraham was like Charles in temperament, and Jeanne could see him settling in Grand-Pré, but she knew this was not what Joseph wanted.

Uncle Abraham spoke up. "Joseph, I think I know how you feel, but consider your wife and children."

"Uncle, I'm not about to go and do anything foolhardy," Joseph said. "But I'm a caboteur like my father before me and I want to continue my trade as long as I can. There must be money to be made in these circumstances. Besides, I think it's too soon to be making big decisions. I'd like to wait and see what happens. We could consider going to Île Saint-Jean. That would be easier for me. I know, I know," he quickly added, "I am considering that my family is safe here for now."

Uncle Abraham attempted to calm the discussion and said, "Well, let's wait and see. Joseph is right. We must wait and see what happens now. At least you are safe here."

Jeanne knew that early in the spring Joseph had carried a message from Louis Du Pont Duchambon, the commandant at Louisbourg, to Paul Marin de la Malgue in Acadia to ask for help for the besieged town. After the fall of the fortress, William Pepperrell, the leader of the New England forces, had asked Joseph to encourage the Acadians in Nova Scotia to send supplies to Louisbourg for the occupying forces. He asked Jeanne to read the messages. He needed to be sure of the contents. When she had started to ask him why, he brusquely interrupted, "Don't ask, Jeanne." She questioned his motives only in silence.

When Joseph returned from his next voyage, he reported that some Mi'kmaq from Île Royale had attacked his schooner at Tatamagouche and threatened him.

"The Mi'kmaq, Joseph, but why?" Jeanne was shocked. "They are our friends."

"Yes, but they are not friendly with the British. I have to respect their wishes. We'll see what happens."

Joseph explained to Jeanne that the Mi'kmaq were more loyal to France than many Acadians were. When word got to the Mi'kmaq some years earlier that the Acadians might take the full oath of allegiance to the British, it was clear that they would consider this a betrayal. In a way, they were right. The full oath would have put the Acadians in a position where they might have had to fight against the French and the Mi'kmaq. The earlier oath, one of neutrality, exempted the Acadians from fighting. Truth be known, only the French version of the oath specified this.

Jeanne was fairly certain that Joseph was not conducting any more business for the British at Île Royale. He kept up his activities, but on a much reduced scale. She was glad for his wife's sake, because she had noticed that Marguerite looked pinched and worried when Joseph was away.

—

There was no further discussion of the matter of whether they should stay in Grand-Pré. Now, when the men gathered for their frequent sessions around the table, they seemed to have reached an uneasy truce. The summer and fall were busy with planting and harvest, and work on the aboiteaux, the system of dykes that provided their rich farmland. All the men pitched in, including Joseph when he was home.

During the winter, Monsieur de la Tour fell ill. Maman spent all her time nursing him. The surgeon came, but was not able to determine what ailed him. "Has he had some tragic news? Is he sick at heart?" the surgeon asked.

Maman explained that they had fled Louisbourg and that her husband had found the recent events hard to accept.

"Ah, well, yes, we all feel that way," the surgeon said.

In early May, when nature was just starting to turn Acadia into a green garden, Monsieur de la Tour passed away.

—

The news from Île Royale in the spring was discouraging. Louisbourg was being manned by a troop of two thousand New Englanders. They had expected to go home after the fighting was over, but had been forced to remain for a year, until British regulars could be sent to relieve them. The New Englanders were expected to repair and rebuild the damaged fortifications, but in the harsh climate and the poor living conditions, many of them had fallen ill. More than a thousand of them died during that first winter.

In mid-summer, Maman herself took sick and was moved to Uncle Abraham's home so that Jeanne could care for her. She had pains in her abdomen and none of the herbs or potions they tried could help. Despite the encouragement her children tried to give her, Maman seemed to have accepted that her time to die had come. Jeanne spent long hours at her bedside. As long as Maman wanted to talk, Jeanne encouraged her to tell stories about her old life in Acadia.

"It broke my heart," she said, "when my three little girls died in Port Toulouse and then baby Étienne in Louisbourg. And now Angélique is lost to us. I hope you will not lose any children, my little Jeanne, but if it happens remember that it is in the hands of le bon Dieu. And you must go on."

"Yes, Maman. You must stop worrying about us," Jeanne chided.

"Ah, Jeanne, that is what mothers do. We believed, your father and I, that we had prepared the way for a good life for all of you. I know that you are all very capable, but you have no control over the events taking place now. And only God knows how all this will end – if even He knows. I believe that Charles and Abraham will be reasonable men and accept whatever comes their way. Joseph is the one likely to take risks, and it worries me greatly." She smiled. "You know, he is the one most like your father. I know you are close to him, Jeanne. Will you try to protect him?"

"Yes, of course, Maman. I'll do all I can."

"Ah, my child. I have no right to ask that of you. You have your own life to live. You are becoming a lovely woman, Jeanne. To think that it was only two years ago, when you surprised Monsieur de la Tour and me by asking for a French-style gown, I could see you settling down as a proper gentlewoman in Louisbourg."

"It's all right, Maman. I believe I'm getting my wish – to be a real Acadian." Jeanne smiled in turn. "And I promise I'll help Joseph all I can, Maman. I worry about him too."

In early September, Maman lost consciousness and a week later she quietly slipped away. They buried her beside Monsieur de la Tour, not far from Angélique's resting place in the Saint-Charles-des-Mines cemetery.

Chapter 13

Another winter passed. The spring of 1747 brought no definite news. The war over the Austrian Succession that had brought about the defeat of Louisbourg was still being fought in Europe. An expedition launched by the French to recapture Louisbourg one year after its defeat had failed, due to storms, disease and attacks by the British navy before the French ships had even reached Île Royale. But this had not totally crushed the hope held by Acadians like Joseph, his father-in-law Le Maigre and his nephew Duvivier that France might yet defeat her enemy. The reports on the progress of the war were now ambiguous enough to leave the outcome uncertain.

The deaths of Maman and Monsieur de la Tour had saddened the families, but it had also brought them closer together. The de la Tour children, Marie and Louise, and the twins, Charlotte and Anne, were now firmly ensconced with Charles's family. There was less talk of leaving Grand-Pré, but Jeanne knew that the question still preoccupied Joseph.

In the spring, Joseph and Marguerite welcomed twins Joseph fils and Marie. This caused great excitement. The birth was a difficult one, and for a while they feared for Marguerite's life, but she survived. Because she was very weak for some months after, many hands cared for the new babies.

—

The spring of 1748 brought more of the same news about the war, but with it came a rumour that an end to hostilities was expected soon. Summer brought news that fighting had ceased in Europe and negotiations for a treaty were underway. The Treaty of Aix-la-Chapelle was signed in October 1748, too late for the news to arrive in Grand-Pré before winter. Although there were plenty of rumours, no one knew for sure what lay in store.

The event of the year for the Dugas was the marriage of Abraham to Marguerite Leblanc (no relation to Joseph Leblanc dit Le Maigre). Abraham had decided to cast his lot with his brother Charles and settle in Grand-Pré, deciding to start his own farm and raise his family there. He would also undertake some cabotage activities on a small scale.

—

In the spring of 1749, the colonies learned that Île Royale had been returned to France under the terms of the Treaty of Aix-la-Chapelle, in exchange for the return of Madras, Spain, to Britain and the withdrawal of French troops from the Low Countries of Europe. The decision to return Louisbourg to France met with strong opposition in Britain and even stronger protests from the New England colonies, who felt that the defeat of Louisbourg in 1745 had been accomplished with the blood and sweat of their men. Both sides knew that the new treaty would not bring a permanent settlement between Britain and France. In fact, it was more a truce than a treaty.

Joseph was cautiously pleased at the news, but disgusted at what he saw as the treatment of Île Royale as a pawn in a game. "De la Tour was right," he grumbled, "we mean nothing to the mother countries. It's too bad he's not here to say I told you so!"

Nevertheless, Joseph started to make plans to return to Louisbourg and this caused great concern for the family. It was as if all the arguments they had stifled while events unfolded now came bubbling out.

Their uncle Abraham begged for caution. "You don't know what you're going to find there," he said. "When is Louisbourg to be turned over? You don't want to arrive there before the French have secured it. You just don't know what you'll find."

"No, Uncle. But I won't know unless I go."

Charles sided with Uncle Abraham and could not understand Joseph's need to leave a secure place for an unknown and risky adventure. Their brother Abraham had made his decision and he intended to stay in Grand-Pré.

Jeanne asked, "Joseph, what about Marguerite and the children?" Joseph's wife was heavy with child again. He could go without her, but what if he did not come back?

"I know, Jeanne," Joseph said. "I'm making plans, but I'm not going right away."

Three weeks later, Marguerite gave birth to a baby girl they named Françoise. As with the birth of the twins, Marguerite's recovery was even slower this time. They expected her to recover as she had before, but about a month after giving birth, Marguerite died.

It was a blow to all the family. Joseph withdrew into himself. Jeanne tried to speak to him, but he brusquely turned her away. When he saw tears in her eyes, he relented.

"I'm sorry, Jeanne. You must know I blame myself for Marguerite's death. I know I did not cause it directly, but I could have been a better husband and father. I was away too often and too long. My Marguerite was so good and kind. What will I do without her?"

"Joseph, it's for you to decide. You know everyone here will help you as much as we can. What will you do? Are you going to go to Louisbourg and leave your children here?" This seemed to pierce Joseph's preoccupation with his grief. He gave Jeanne a stricken look, then turned and walked away.

Several weeks later, when it was clear that the new baby Françoise was thriving, Joseph told Jeanne that he would make a voyage to Louisbourg in the summer, to see how things were there, and then he would decide what to do. He also told Jeanne that he had been approached by a niece, Marie Braud, who offered her services to help with the children. Marie had been born with a club foot and then orphaned when she was only five years old. Joseph felt that hers was a difficult life and that she would be of great help if taken in.

"It would be too much for you, Jeanne," he said. "You should not have all these children to look after." ·

Chapter 14

In the summer of 1749, Joseph repaired his schooner, the *Marie-Josèphe*, the one the Mi'kmaq had attacked in Tatamagouche, and he sailed for Île Royale. At Louisbourg, he found that his home on rue Royalle was badly damaged and uninhabitable. It had been requisitioned as part of the British colonial governor's quarters during the New England occupation and later used as a storehouse. Understandably, conditions in Louisbourg were still unsettled.

On his way back to Grand-Pré, Joseph stopped at Port Toulouse to check on the land his father had left to the family.

He knew that after the defeat of Louisbourg in 1745, the New England forces had attacked Port Toulouse and the surrounding area, burning down the town, the fort and the brickworks. They even desecrated a Mi'kmaw burial ground. Many of the settlers had left, and any who remained were caught and killed or taken prisoner and deported.

Joseph found that most of the land his father had cleared nearly forty years ago was again covered with fir trees – the two dwellings mainly in ruins. But he discovered that other Acadians were returning to the area, and that Louisbourg was again sending some French troops there. This was encouraging. It did not lift his spirits, but he decided it would be a safer place to settle than Louisbourg.

When he announced his intention to move to Port Toulouse and to take his children with him, his brothers and his uncle Abraham tried to disuade him. But Joseph would not be swayed. He asked Marie Braud if she would go with them and she agreed.

At Joseph's announcement the family turned their eyes on Jeanne. They knew she was very attached to her brother and his children.

Before she could speak, Joseph said, "Jeanne, you can make a good life for yourself here in Grand-Pré. You must stay."

She knew he was sincere, and of course everyone else joined in to agree with him. But she was very unsettled by the situation. "I don't know," she said and frowned. "I have to think about it." Then she walked out of the room.

She had a favourite place on Uncle Abraham's farm where she liked to go when she had to think about something important. It was between the house and the barn, in a slight hollow, where someone had placed a bench beside a willow tree. She went there now, just to sit and think. She had never before had to make such an important decision for herself.

—

Since losing their father, Jeanne's brother Joseph had been the anchor in her life, perhaps even more so since Maman had died. And she had promised Maman that she would try to protect him. Now she wondered exactly what Maman had meant. Jeanne knew she could stay in Grand-Pré and that she would find a suitable husband here, but was this what she wanted? Sometimes she wondered if perhaps she was a kindred soul to Joseph and like him not afraid to take risks.

The following day she announced that she would go with Joseph, and she made it clear that she was going as much for herself as for Joseph and his children. Marie Braud looked stricken for a moment, but Jeanne said with a smile, "No, Marie, you are to come too. I'm sure there will plenty to keep us both busy." When Joseph opened his mouth to protest, Jeanne told him, "No, my mind is made up and as you know I am a truly stubborn Acadienne." The rest of the family knew it was pointless to argue with her.

—

They sailed for Port Toulouse in mid-September, Joseph, his five children – all under eight years of age – and Jeanne and Marie Braud. As their schooner set sail, all of them were on deck to wave good-bye to their relatives – some of them crying. Jeanne was afraid but also strangely elated. She was embarking on an adventure on the sea she loved.

Their arrival at Port Toulouse was not encouraging. Jeanne had never been there, but when she saw the two dilapidated habitations on her father's property and felt the dampness in the air, she knew how her mother must have felt when she had arrived there many years before. They quickly set to work to repair the houses and clear some ground.

Jeanne and Marie made the best of it, but it was clear that Joseph was not happy. He was bitter at France's lack of support for its colony during the siege of Louisbourg and at its cavalier attitude in using Île Royale as a mere pawn in the Treaty of Aix-la-Chapelle. Would the mother country treat its colony any better now?

In October, to Jeanne's dismay, Joseph's father-in-law Joseph Leblanc dit Le Maigre arrived in Port Toulouse. For all his cabotage activities before and during the war, he was now penniless.

In fact, his activities on behalf of the French in 1745 had led to his capture and imprisonment by the British. He had apparently been held in chains in a terrible dungeon for six months, and his attempts to engage in business activities after his release from prison had all failed miserably. The man once considered the wealthiest man in Acadia now accepted the stipend the French crown was still offering to Acadians to settle on Île Royale.

Now in his fifties, Joseph Leblanc arrived with his wife, Anne Bourg; their three youngest children, Alexandre, Paul and Anne; his eighty-one-year-old father-in-law; a young nephew, Joseph; and a niece, Marie-Josée Alain. As well as being very large in his person, everything about Joseph Leblanc dit Le Maigre seemed larger than life. He was expansive and disruptive. Or so it seemed to Jeanne.

Joseph gave his father-in-law one of the habitations on the property for his use, and Joseph's family began to share with the Leblancs the provisions they had brought with them from Grand-Pré. Jeanne said nothing, but of course Joseph knew how she felt. One day he said, "Well, what do you expect me to do?" Jeanne just shrugged.

There was not much time for petty grievances. The necessities of life were not as abundant here as in Grand-Pré. They managed to get through the winter, using the stock of provisions they had brought with them, supplemented by hunting small animals such as hare, partridge and woodcock. In the spring, they planted a kitchen garden and started to clear more land. Eventually, Joseph would have two arpents planted with turnips he hoped to sell – but crops were meagre. In the summer, fish was plentiful in both the lakes and the sea, and they managed to salt enough codfish for their own use. Their farm animals grew to include an ox, two cows, two pigs and twelve chickens.

The children adapted themselves, as children do. Jeanne and Marie worked hard and Joseph did his best to be a good father. But in the evening when the children were asleep, he became silent and brooding. Jeanne knew that her brother was preoccupied with the political situation and frustrated with his life as a farmer at Port Toulouse. He had done little coastal trading since the unpleasant incident at Tatamagouche when the Mi'kmaq had attacked his boat and menaced him. Jeanne wondered how long he would go on this way.

The Mi'kmaq had left their summer encampment near Port Toulouse soon after the Dugas arrived in the fall, so Joseph had not had much contact with them. When they returned in the spring, they brought with them one of the former scouts at Louisbourg, Jean Sauvage. Joseph was very happy to see him again, not only for news but also because they were friends in the years leading up to the defeat of the fortress. Jean Sauvage had heard of Joseph's encounter with the angry Mi'kmaq at Tatamagouche, but now told him not to worry about it. He also reported that life was only slowly returning to normal for the French at Louisbourg and he warned that there was still a fair amount of activity by British privateers around Île Royale. He promised to keep Joseph informed of any events around the island.

There were incidents with British privateers. The summer after their return, Joseph Leblanc dit Le Maigre was captured by privateers and held prisoner for eight days. The British privateers released him and his several companions unharmed, but they lost the shallop they were travelling in and all the goods it contained.

Jeanne was aware of the long discussions that Joseph and his father-in-law had that sometimes verged on bitter arguments. Le Maigre, like Joseph, was not well suited to the life of a farmer. He was unable to acquire land of his own at Port

Toulouse, although he managed to acquire twenty-five cows and ten chickens during the three years he received his stipend from the crown.

The settlers now in Port Toulouse were Acadians returning to their homes or displaced from other areas. One family they met, that of Pierre Bois and his wife Marie Coste, were originally from Ardoise in Nova Scotia. They had first settled in Port Toulouse decades ago, and they remembered Joseph Dugas père and his wife Marguerite Richard. Jeanne was touched to meet someone who had known her parents and she became friends with the family.

—

The first two years in Port Toulouse went by quickly, preoccupied as they all were with adjusting to living in reduced circumstances. Once in a while, if she had a quiet moment, Jeanne would take her blue gown out of its bundle and run her hands over the soft silk. Then she would unwrap the portrait the Louisbourg artist had painted of her. She marvelled at how innocent she looked, her face unblemished, her hands soft. Now, only a few years later, her complexion was dark from exposure to the sun as she worked in the garden and the barnyard, and her hands were red and roughened. *I am barely twenty years old*, she thought, *but soon I will look like an old woman.*

One day Joseph caught her by surprise as she was looking at the portrait. She must have looked sad. He said, "Jeanne, you're just as beautiful now."

She shook her head and could not help the tear that escaped and ran down her cheek. "I'm all right, Joseph," she said. He looked stricken.

"Jeanne, you can go back to Grand-Pré, you know," he said quietly. "You've done so much for us, but we can manage now. I'll take you back." But Jeanne knew that sailing to Grand-Pré at this time was dangerous, especially for Joseph. He and his father-in-law were known to be French supporters. The British authorities in Acadia did not trust Acadians who supported the French cause, any more than did the Mi'kmaq.

It seemed to Jeanne that Joseph was particularly concerned about his relations with the Mi'kmaq. There was a lot of communication between the Acadians at Port Toulouse and the Mi'kmaq while they were camped by the ocean in the summer. And Joseph kept in close touch with Jean Sauvage. He was older than Joseph, and Jeanne's brother respected and looked up to him. Joseph said one day that he admired the way the Mi'kmaq lived – off the intelligence of the land – and the way they respected that land and all of God's creatures on it.

On one of his frequent visits to the Dugas habitation, Jean Sauvage brought his nephew with him. Martin Sauvage was a few years older than Jeanne, and she thought he must be the most handsome man she had ever seen. He was tall and slim, with strong, regular features set in the serious expression of the Mi'kmaq. Only when he smiled or laughed did his expression change, and it had the effect of a bright sun breaking through clouds. Jeanne surprised herself with this image, and chided herself for thinking such thoughts. Sometimes Martin came to visit on his own, but always for a purpose – to bring a gift of berries or a fish he had caught.

—

Life went on. Joseph and his father-in-law continued to talk about the political situation and how they could take advantage of events to return to their lucrative cabotage activities. Le Maigre had no ship, and no means to buy one, but Joseph still had one schooner.

Chapter 15

The news from Nova Scotia was worrisome. The Acadians were once again concerned about their status in the now-British colony. In 1749, after the return of Île Royale to the French, the new British governor, Edward Cornwallis, had arrived in the colony with plans to establish a new fort at Halifax and to bring in a large number of new settlers. It was intended as a counterbalance to Louisbourg and as protection for British trade with the English colonies.

Uncertain of their standing, a group of Acadians from Nova Scotia approached the Governor with an offer to renew the conditional oath of allegiance sworn to earlier. Cornwallis demanded that they now sign an unconditional oath of allegiance that would oblige them to bear arms for the British crown. They refused, and the British authorities would not listen to their arguments.

The arrogant new Governor also incurred the wrath of the Mi'kmaq. They had approached the Governor in a friendly manner, expressing their concern that he was proposing to build his fort and settlement on land that they had been living on for many years and that was sacred to them. The Governor ignored their request for a discussion on the matter.

He decided that the best way to deal with the Mi'kmaq was to simply eliminate them from the land. He announced his plan to destroy them with a proclamation stating that the British would "pursue them to their haunts and show them that because of such actions, they shall not be secure within the Province ... and that a reward of ten Guineas be granted for every Indian Micmac taken, or killed." There were rumours that in the ensuing bloodletting, some Acadian scalps also found their way into the Governor's hands. He did not succeed in destroying the Mi'kmaq, who despite their gentle nature were also fierce warriors. And he made an enemy.

Chapter 16

J oseph had continued his habit of taking Jeanne into his confidence on political events ever since she was a little girl, and now he told her that if Louisbourg and Île Royale fell once more to the British, they probably would not find refuge in Grand-Pré.

"Where will we go, Joseph?"

He just shrugged. The confident brother who had reassured and protected Jeanne through the fall of Louisbourg was now admitting his uncertainty.

"It will be all right," she said. "You'll see." It seemed that the tables were turned, with Jeanne trying to give her brother comfort and reassurance. But she knew they were just words.

—

In the spring of 1752, on one of her visits to the Bois family, Jeanne expressed her worries. Marie tried to reassure her. "You must have faith," she said. "We are all in the same situation. Remember that your brother Joseph is a very capable man."

Pierre fils, Marie's son, joined in the conversation, he too trying to calm her fears.

Annoyed, she thought to herself, *It's his inexperience speaking.* Jeanne had thought of young Pierre Bois as just a boy when she arrived in Port Toulouse. Now he was starting to take on the appearance of a man. When she left to return home, he told her he would accompany her.

"Yes," his mother said, "go with her, Pierre. You should not be walking home alone, Jeanne. It's really not safe."

They walked back in companionable silence. As they were approaching her house, Pierre stopped and took her hand.

"Jeanne," he said, "there's something I've been wanting to ask you." He looked down at the ground. "I'm a man now." He looked up at her.

"Really. And I think it's time for me to take a wife." He paused, as if waiting for some word of encouragement. But Jeanne was silent.

"I think you would make a wonderful wife. Would you think about it? Consider marrying me?"

Jeanne laughed nervously, not knowing what to say. He let go of her hand.

"Pierre, I'm sorry. I wasn't laughing at you. I'm sure you will make some lucky girl a wonderful husband. But my brother Joseph needs me. I can't just walk away from him and his family. And I'm older than you are, Pierre," she said with a smile, trying to make light of his proposal.

"What does that matter?" he asked. "Please think about it, Jeanne? Please?" She nodded hesitantly and watched him walk away.

Jeanne was dumbfounded. The thought of Pierre Bois as a man and possible suitor had never occurred to her. She did not want to hurt his feelings, and hoped he would simply forget about this.

He did not try to rush her into changing her mind, but he kept in contact with Joseph and his family, which included her. Pierre told Joseph that he was hoping to become a cabo-teur. He had already worked as a deckhand for several seasons on schooners sailing out of Port Toulouse, saving the money he earned toward building a ship of his own. Of course Joseph encouraged him. He even suggested that he could perhaps use Pierre as part of his crew if he started trading again.

Jeanne was uncomfortable. She could not very well object to Pierre's presence without explaining herself, which she did not want to do. To complicate matters, Martin Sauvage was also becoming a frequent visitor to the Dugas habitation, and Jeanne had to admit, if only to herself, that her heart beat faster at the sight of him.

Marie Braud understood what was happening and gently teased Jeanne one day. When Jeanne snapped at her, she said she was sorry. "I only wish I had two suitors," Marie said with a sigh.

Joseph finally caught on to the situation one day.

"Jeanne," he said, "why am I running into either Pierre Bois bringing us vegetables from his mother's garden, or Martin Sauvage bringing us still more berries?"

Jeanne blushed and Marie Braud hid a smile.

"Ah, Jeanne ... Jeanne." Joseph did not know what to say. He put his arm around her shoulders with a gentle squeeze. "We will talk later."

Mon Dieu, she thought, *I've given Joseph another problem to add to everything else*. Honestly, she did not even know what she herself wanted. But did it matter?

That evening, after the children and Marie were asleep, Joseph approached her. "Well, Jeanne...."

Yes, she thought, *Well, Jeanne* ... and could not help but blurt out: "What? Are you asking me to explain to you what I feel? I don't even know myself. I don't even know from one day to the other what my life is or will be. I don't know who or what I am most of the time. Oh, I'm sorry, Joseph, I'm really sorry. None of this is your fault. And I'm not sorry that I came here with you."

She paused and continued in a calmer voice, looking at him very seriously, "I do know, Joseph, that if I don't marry, I'll be just another person you have to look after when your children are grown and you don't need me anymore."

"Jeanne! Don't speak like that!" he said angrily. Then he was silent for a short while, allowing some time for the two of them to calm down.

"Jeanne, you know I only want what is best for you. And I think you know that I would do anything I can to make you happy. But you know as well as I do that these are difficult times."

"Yes, I know that very well, Joseph. So tell me, does that mean that I had better marry the first man who asks me?"

"Has Pierre asked you to marry him?"

"Yes."

"Has Martin?"

"No." There was a glimmer of a tear in her eye.

"Have you asked yourself what Maman would say?"

"No. I don't think she would understand. She thought I would marry a rich man in Louisbourg and lead the life of a gentlewoman." Jeanne smiled wryly. "And here I am. It's not fair, Joseph. You and Charles and Abraham have all married girls you loved."

"Yes, I know, Jeanne. And I can understand that you are attracted to Martin Sauvage. I believe he is a very fine man. I like him very much. But, quite apart from the fact that he is Mi'kmaw and you would have to adapt to his family's way of life, there is also the dangerous political situation the Mi'kmaq are in now. Martin is a good and gentle man, but he is also a warrior. If the fighting continues between the Mi'kmaq and the British, there is no telling what may happen to him, or to you. I'm sure he understands that."

"But it's not fair, Joseph."

"No, Jeanne, it isn't. If life were fair, we would not be in this situation. You would be wearing beautiful silk gowns with hoop skirts and fighting off wealthy suitors in Louisbourg." Joseph was trying to make her smile. "What about Pierre Bois?"

"I don't know, Joseph."

"Why not? He's Acadian," Joseph said with a smile. "He's young, ambitious and energetic. He annoys me at times, but I think his heart is in the right place."

"Is that your way of saying that he's not quite up to the standards that you and Maman and Monsieur de la Tour would have wanted for me? He's not even from a well-to-do Acadian family. Mon Dieu, how can we even think that way now?"

"Jeanne, think about all this for awhile. You don't have to decide right this minute. In the meantime," he said with a smile, "we'll keep getting a good supply of vegetables and berries."

"Joseph, that's not funny."

"Yes, it is. Go to bed, Jeanne."

She lay awake thinking for a long time. Now she had two distinct worries on her mind. First, what might be the consequences of the worsening political situation if Louisbourg again fell to the British. If they could not take refuge in Grand-Pré, where could they go to avoid deportation to France? In this case, if even in her own mind the possibility of her marrying Martin was very remote, as the wife of a Mi'kmaq would she perhaps avoid deportation? Second, what might be the consequences if she married Pierre Bois? For instance, would this mean separation from Joseph and his family if they had to flee?

Joseph knew she was worried. One day he rubbed the frown from her brow as he used to do when she was a little girl. "I'm sorry, Jeanne," he said.

—

That year Joseph started his trading activities again, with his father-in-law Joseph Leblanc dit Le Maigre as a partner and Pierre Bois included as a member of the crew. At first Joseph tried to re-establish the kind of trade he had been doing when he was based at Louisbourg, but he found it difficult after his years away. It was not long, however, before he tapped into a newly lucrative trade – transporting Acadians from Nova Scotia to Île Saint-Jean. After the signing of the Treaty of Utrecht in 1713, the small number of Acadians who left the new British colony of Nova Scotia had gone mainly to Île Royale. Now, with the fate of Île Royale once again in doubt, Île Saint-Jean seemed a better choice.

The Acadians now fleeing Nova Scotia were doing so il-legally, but with the encouragement of the French authorities, who were anxious to increase the number of French settlers on Île Saint-Jean. To this end the French were offering to pay the Acadians' passages and to give them a stipend to help their resettlement.

This was a dangerous form of cabotage, but Joseph and others would make several hundred crossings carrying refu-gees and food supplies to the island from the Tatamagouche area of Nova Scotia. It not only paid well, but Jeanne could see her brother come alive again. It was clear that he loved be-ing on the sea, that he loved the risks involved and the feeling of playing a part in the unfolding events.

It became another source of worry for Jeanne. What would happen to them if Joseph were captured, or injured or lost at sea?

She again confided her fears to Pierre's mother, but Marie Bois had only a very vague idea of the political situation. Her life revolved around her husband, their large brood of children and her faith that all would be well. She was not unsympathetic to Jeanne's fears and worries, but seemed to think it unseemly for a young woman to be so concerned. She was also, Jeanne knew, all in favour of having Jeanne for a daughter-in-law and praised her son Pierre's virtues every chance she got.

Before he left to crew on Joseph's schooner, Pierre again approached Jeanne to ask for her hand in marriage. This time he was bolder. He told her he loved her very much.

"I'm afraid I was not very clear when I spoke to you before," he said. "I didn't just mean I needed a wife. I meant that I wanted very much to have *you* for my wife. Will you please consider marrying me, Jeanne? Seriously? I do love you, Jeanne."

She told him, "I cannot give you an answer yet, Pierre." She knew this was unfair. She had no intention of marrying him.

—

When the sailing season closed in the fall, Pierre brought her a gift he had obtained from another ship. It was a length of yellow silk suitable for a gown. It was not the quality of her blue silk gown, but it made Jeanne catch her breath. She was touched by the gesture.

"I know it's not as beautiful as your blue silk gown," he said.

"How do you know about my gown?" she asked.

"Joseph told me."

She wondered if Joseph had also told him that she wanted to marry for love.

"I'm going to start building my boat this winter, Jeanne. My father and grandfather are going to help me." His grandfather Jean Coste, his mother's father, was well known as a superb navigator and shipbuilder.

Jeanne confided in Marie Braud, who could not understand Jeanne's reluctance to marry Pierre. "I would have him to husband in a wink," she said.

Martin Sauvage had not been seen for months.

—

The end of the sailing season also brought the news that a new Governor of Nova Scotia had been appointed in August. Peregrine Hopson was known to the settlers. He had been sent to relieve the British garrison at Louisbourg in 1746 and was in command when it was returned to the French in 1749. He was known as a reasonable man, a facilitator and a conciliator. His return from England to be the governor was generally seen as a good omen by both the Acadians and the Mi'kmaq.

"Ah, Joseph, is that some good news at last?" Jeanne asked.

"I cannot lie to you, Jeanne. The situation is still serious." Joseph added that he had managed to see their brother Charles during the season. Charles had told him that if things became too difficult they were planning to flee Grand-Pré to go the Miramichi area beyond Nova Scotia. He had suggested that Joseph and his family should join them.

"Joseph," Jeanne said hesitantly, "Pierre has again asked me to marry him. And he said he loves me. Did you have anything to do with that?"

Joseph smiled. "I *know* he loves you very much, Jeanne. I may have encouraged him to say it. But how do you feel about him?"

"I guess I love him a little bit. Do you think I should marry him?"

"Jeanne, it is for you to make that decision. You are a very intelligent woman. A strong woman. You do what you feel is right and that way you will never regret it."

"I think ... I think I will marry him."

"You're sure?"

"Yes."

"Good! Now maybe you should tell him."

When Pierre appeared at the door the next day and looked at her expectantly, she said, "Yes, I will marry you, Pierre." He gave a whoop and swept her into a hug. He was a bit shorter than her, but she found that she fit quite well into his arms. "Will you come with me to tell my family?" he asked. Joseph accompanied them.

The Bois family was delighted with the news, especially Pierre's mother. Her son was the first boy after four girls, and Jeanne knew he was very special to her. Everybody started to speak at once, making plans for the happy event. At the end of the day, there were plans for a wedding to take place just before the start of Advent, plans to build a piquet house for the new couple on the Dugas land, and promises from Pierre's father and grandfather Coste that the new schooner would be ready in the spring.

Jeanne allowed herself to get caught up in the excitement. Yet, lying awake on her paillasse that night, she had the same sense she had had during her family's last year in Louisbourg – that she was living on two levels: one the happy events of the day and the other the dark cloud of uncertainty hanging over all of them.

With the sailing and harvesting seasons over, their neighbours joined the Dugas and Bois men in a houseraising. The new piquet house was built near Joseph's and his father-in-law's habitations. Joseph and Pierre's father made a table and benches, a bedstead and other simple furniture. Pierre's mother fashioned a straw paillasse and provided some linens. In the meantime, Pierre and grandfather Coste started to work on Pierre's new schooner.

Joseph had seen his brothers Charles and Abraham in Grand-Pré during the summer and told them of the possibility of Jeanne's marriage. On their last meeting the two brothers sent Joseph back laden with gifts from Grand-Pré, including linen and woollen goods, dishes and provisions of grains and other foodstuffs from their gardens. Joseph also gave generously, of course, providing the couple with two cows and one hen.

Pierre radiated happiness. He was full of plans for their future. It seemed to Jeanne that she was the only one who was apprehensive. Everyone was so excited and happy that she eventually let herself be carried along and almost forgot her worries.

—

In early December of 1752, on the eve of Advent, Jeanne Dugas and Pierre Bois fils were united in marriage by the Recollet missionary at Port Toulouse, Père Chérubin Ropert. It was a festive occasion for the small community. Just about everyone participated, including a number of Mi'kmaw friends, among them Jean Sauvage. There was no mention of his nephew Martin. After the religious ceremony, everyone gathered at the Dugas compound to share food and music. As relatives and friends started to leave, Jeanne saw tears in Marie Braud's eyes. She was touched by this, although in her heart Jeanne thought that Marie was also pleased that she would now be the only woman in Joseph's habitation. She understood.

—

Their first winter as a couple passed quickly. Pierre spent all the daylight hours working on his new schooner with his father and grandfather. Jeanne was busy putting her new home in order. By the end of January in the new year, she knew she was expecting a child. Pierre was thrilled. Jeanne's first reaction was that she now had a new source for worry. What kind of world would this new Acadian baby face? She felt safe for the moment, with Pierre, her large family of in-laws and her brother Joseph nearby. But what if political events again forced them to flee?

She did not share her worries with Pierre, who at times seemed to expect her to be more like his mother. He simply assumed that his wife would leave the worrying to the men and concern herself only with her children and the confines of their habitation. Jeanne did not hold this against him. She realized he did not understand her need to know and comprehend the events happening in the outside world.

Pierre had been surprised to learn that Jeanne could read and write. She smiled as she remembered his reaction. He had looked at her as if she were some strange kind of being. She had reassured him that this was a good quality to have. She could help him with contracts when he became a caboteur with his own ship.

She kept her precious books, her blue silk gown, her necklace, her embroidered shawl, her portrait and the length of yellow silk given to her by Pierre in a bundle discreetly hidden at the bottom of a wooden chest. She had no use for these things now, but she would cling to them as long as she could. They were a link to a very different past and to the life she might have had.

Chapter 17

When spring 1753 arrived, Jeanne was determined to face life serenely. She was now a married woman, with her own home, and expecting her first child. Pierre's schooner would not be finished before mid-summer, but he was happy with its progress. In the meantime he was happy to help Jeanne with the garden and the farm animals while he was at home. She could not have asked for a better husband, she thought, although she wished her mother-in-law would stop reminding her of this.

Late in the afternoon of a beautiful day in the first week of June, when Port Toulouse and its surrounding area was freshly green again, Jeanne went for a walk in the nearby woods, looking for mayflowers. Wrapped in her thoughts, she was suddenly aware of a presence near her, and turned around to find Martin. He was holding out a small bunch of mayflowers to her. "I thought you would be looking for these," he said.

"Martin," she said, reaching out a hand to take the flowers and then withdrawing it and guiltily covering her stomach with both hands. He calmly took in her gesture.

"Jeanne, your brother told me that you are married to Pierre. And expecting your first child. I am very happy for you."

Of course, she should have known that Martin would be so kind. But why was she disappointed? Would she prefer to see him angry?

"Thank you," she said. *Oh, why was this so difficult?* she thought. "You've been away for a long time, Martin."

"Yes. I've been away helping my people." She looked at him enquiringly. "I cannot tell you about it. Please," he said, extending the flowers.

"Thank you, Martin." She took the posy of mayflowers and buried her nose in them, letting the delicate petals and sweet aroma permeate her senses and hide her feelings.

"Let me walk back with you, Jeanne. You shouldn't be here alone." He walked her to the edge of the clearing surrounding her house.

"Will I see you again?" she asked.

"Yes," he nodded, and walked away.

After a moment she turned to see him and caught him looking at her with an expression, she imagined, of longing and pain. But he noticed her and his usual calm mask quickly took over. She continued back to the house.

—

In mid-summer Pierre launched his schooner, the *Angélique*. Asked to name the ship, Jeanne had chosen her late sister's name. Père Ropert came to bless the *Angélique* on the day of her maiden voyage. There was much excitement as Jeanne, her many in-laws, Marie Braud and Joseph's children came to the port to see the ship off. Pierre stood proudly at the prow, his eyes fixed on the horizon, master of his ship as the sail unfurled and billowed. His grandfather Coste stood beside him, equally proud. Jeanne stood on the wharf and watched the new schooner until it faded away on the horizon, her thoughts on what the future might bring.

The remainder of the summer passed without incident. Pierre managed to get a few small contracts to transport freight to Louisbourg. Jeanne knew he had hoped to do better, but she was not displeased. His trips were shorter and safer than those Joseph took. Since she was a young child Jeanne had heard the stories of ships and their captains lost at sea, their widows left mourning on the shore. She now understood the anxiety.

—

In mid-October, when the sailing season was coming to an end and Joseph was on his last voyage, Pierre had an opportunity to do one more trip. He was reluctant to go, because he knew that it would soon be time for Jeanne to deliver the baby, but he sorely wanted the money this last trip would bring. He asked for Jeanne's opinion. What could she say? Not even Pierre's mother suggested that he should refuse the trip for Jeanne's sake. So she told him to go. He assured her he would be back in five days.

Two days after he left, there were rumours that privateers from the New England colonies were prowling close to the shore near Port Toulouse. No doubt they too were trying to profit from the last sailing days of the year, and knew that many of the men of Port Toulouse would still be away. Soon Grandfather Coste arrived at the Dugas farm to report that a privateer ship had landed and ransacked a farm not far from where the Dugas were settled. He persuaded Le Maigre's family and Marie Braud and Joseph's children to flee to the Coste farm, which was farther inland and less likely to be attacked.

Jeanne knew that in her condition she could not walk that far, and certainly not quickly. They would have to try to reach the farm before dark. The baby had fallen in her womb and she realized that her time to give birth was near. She told Grandfather Coste she would go with Marie Braud and told Marie that she would go with the Leblancs. She hoped that in the confusion no one would notice right away that she was missing.

—

That same evening, the pains came. She was afraid. She had carefully prepared the baby's layette and Grandfather Coste had made a cradle for the child, but she was not well prepared to give birth alone. She had heard that sometimes the pains would start and then stop, perhaps for even as long as a day. But as the evening wore on, the pains got stronger.

It was already dark. The small cod oil lamp seemed to cast sinister shadows in her cosy home. She told herself she must be brave and she lay down on the paillasse. She began to pray, but her prayers were interrupted by a moan when a sharp pain seized her. Suddenly, she heard someone at the door. *Ah, mon Dieu*, she thought, *not the privateers.*

The door slowly opened, and in walked Martin.

"Martin?" Of course, he would be the only one walking about after dark.

"Jeanne ... Jeanne ... I saw there was a light." He took in the situation at a glance. "Is the baby coming?"

"Yes."

"Where is everyone?"

"Pierre and Joseph are at sea, and the others have gone to the Coste farm because of the privateers. I knew I couldn't make it with them."

"Ah, Jeanne. How close are the pains?"

"Maybe every quarter hour."

"I'm going to get someone to help you, Jeanne. I won't be long." He put a gentle hand on her cheek. "Everything will be all right."

He returned with a Mi'kmaw woman who took one look at her and shook her head.

"Grandmother has brought many babies into the world," Martin said. "She will take good care of you."

Jeanne felt tears coming.

"I am here, Jeanne."

The midwife did not speak French. She spoke to Martin, who knelt at Jeanne's head and translated her instructions.

"You must be brave, Jeanne." He spoke softly and rubbed her shoulders and soothed her. She felt herself relax, and now as the pains came she was less frightened and the pain did not seem so bad. At last, deep in the night hours, she gave a last push and felt the baby leave her body.

The midwife cut the cord, wiped the baby and rubbed it with oil. Jeanne heard the baby cry. Then the midwife wrapped the baby in a blanket and placed it on Jeanne's stomach. She said something to Martin.

"Grandmother says you have a beautiful and healthy baby girl," he said. "I have to take Grandmother home now, but I will come back."

They left quietly. Jeanne unwrapped the baby to see for herself that she had ten fingers and ten toes. She looked perfect. Now she thought of Pierre.

She felt exhausted and drained after the birth. And hurt at being abandoned. She held the baby and tried not to think. She wasn't sure how long it was before Martin returned.

"Martin, I'm so sorry. I'm so sorry you had to do this."

"Jeanne, I am very happy that I was here to help you. We are special friends, you and I. You must not feel sorry."

At this Jeanne burst into tears and could not stop.

Martin lay down beside her and wrapped his arms around her and the baby. She lay in his arms, her arms around her baby, and sobbed as if her heart would break.

When she had no more tears to shed, she fell into an exhausted sleep, and only woke when she heard the baby cry. Martin still held her in his arms. "I think the baby is hungry," he said. It was daylight.

Martin stayed for a short time, while she nursed the baby, and he found some bread and head cheese for Jeanne to eat. He looked as if he were on the alert. Soon he said, "I think I hear someone." He went outside to check. He always seemed to hear or sense someone or something before it happened.

"Some of your relatives are coming. They must have been very worried about you. I think I should go. Tell them I brought Grandmother to help you." And before she could say anything, he stole away.

Pierre's return from his voyage was delayed. By the time he arrived his new baby girl was ten days old and Jeanne had recovered from her distress. Père Ropert baptized the baby Marie Marguerite for her two grandmothers. She would be known as Marie – petite Marie to distinguish her from her Grandmother Bois.

—

After his last voyage of the season, Joseph reported there were no major changes in the political situation, either good or bad. It appeared that Governor Hopson was trying to repair relations with both the Acadians and the Mi'kmaq after the treatment they had received from Governor Cornwallis, but this was doing little to stem the flow of Acadians leaving Nova Scotia.

Joseph had made more voyages than the previous year. He said he found it difficult to understand why so many Acadians would leave their prosperous farms for an uncertain future on Île Saint-Jean.

He had seen his brothers Charles and Abraham once during the whole summer. They were worried about their future, but had not yet made the decision to leave their farms in Grand-Pré. They reminded him of their plan to seek refuge in the Miramichi area if they decided the situation was dangerous.

"They seem to think that I'm leading a dangerous life," Joseph told Jeanne, "but I think their situation in Nova Scotia is more perilous." Jeanne tended to agree with Charles and Abraham, but she knew Joseph would not change.

—

Once again they faced a winter of silence, closed off from the outside world by ice and snow – a period when all they could do was to ponder their fate. On one hand, there was the general feeling of dread caused by the building of the new British fort at Halifax and the plans to bring in a large number of new settlers. On the other hand, they now hoped to receive fair treatment from Governor Peregrine Hopson. But would this be enough? Jeanne was torn between worrying about how the political situation could affect their lives and worrying about her responsibilities as a wife and mother.

She had grown up in Joseph's confidence. He had kept the promise he made to her when she was very young, that he would keep her informed of political events that could affect their lives, and he had always treated her as an adult. She had lived within the circle of his life, where this information came easily. Now, that had changed. Now, she was a married woman living in her husband's home.

She realized that Joseph, although he had approved of her marriage, did not treat Pierre as an equal. At first she thought it was because of her husband's youthfulness – Joseph, and his father-in-law Le Maigre, were of an older generation. But she came to believe that it was more likely because Pierre did not share their patriotic zeal as Acadians. Yes, Pierre was Acadian and proud of it, but Jeanne was certain that he had never thought in terms of fighting for the Acadian cause. It was obvious that Pierre resented her easy access to her brother and her interest in events in the world outside her habitation, thinking it unseemly in a woman.

Pierre knew that Joseph shared his news and plans with Jeanne, often when Pierre himself was not included in the discussions. And when he had asked Joseph about the possibility of Pierre using his new schooner to transport Acadians, Joseph had discouraged the idea. Jeanne was annoyed with her brother for excluding her husband – after all Joseph was only one of a number of caboteurs profiting from this trade.

Pierre Bois did not lack confidence in himself. As a settler, as an Acadian, as a caboteur and as a family man, Pierre had his own strengths. But Jeanne knew that Joseph's daring, his rashness, his enjoyment of risk, made Pierre look ordinary and plodding. She wished that Joseph could be more understanding.

Joseph understood Jeanne's concerns, and said he would keep her informed of any news he received. With a bitter smile Jeanne told him she would miss him when he left on the spring tides, but she would not miss having to listen to Le Maigre's loud diatribes against the British and almost everyone and everything else.

"I still don't like him," she said.

Chapter 18

Spring of 1754 brought the news that Nova Scotia had had yet another change of governor. Peregine Hopson, on whom many Acadians had pinned their hopes for good governance, had returned to England on the last ship to sail the previous fall. Charles Lawrence had been named Lieutenant-Governor on November 1, 1753 – an appointment that did not bode well for the Acadians. Lawrence had been in the colony since 1749 and he was known to be very much a military man, not a conciliator or facilitator.

"What does this mean, Joseph?" Jeanne asked.

"I'm not sure. We'll have to wait and see. But I know it's going to be a busy summer for the caboteurs."

"It's going to be dangerous too, isn't it? Are you going to let Pierre join you?"

Joseph hesitated, looking at her. "Jeanne, it's not dangerous for someone like me or my father-in-law, because we know the risks. We've made so many voyages. I wouldn't want anything to happen to your husband."

She had known what he would say, but that didn't make it easier for her husband. At least Pierre could get contracts for carrying supplies to Louisbourg.

The men left on their schooners as usual at the beginning of the season. The families went down to the port to see them off on their first voyage.

—

Jeanne saw Martin Sauvage only once that summer, one day when she was out walking with the baby. He must have come up behind her very quietly, then deliberately made a noise so that she would not be startled.

"How is baby Marie?" he asked.

"She is very well," Jeanne replied and handed her to him.

Little Marie, who usually did not take to strangers, first looked at him solemnly with her big brown eyes, and then gave him a smile showing him her two new teeth.

He gave her his special smile in return and said to her, "You know, I was one of the first two people on this earth to see you when you arrived here. You are very beautiful, petite Marie, like your Maman."

Jeanne blushed. Martin smiled, then handed the baby back to her and stole away.

—

The Acadians at Port Toulouse heard many rumours during the first part of the summer and there were many conflicting stories. Jeanne found herself wanting to believe the more hopeful news and to discount the less favourable. Pierre was home between voyages more often than Joseph, but his news of Nova Scotia and the British was second hand. Joseph, whose cargo was Acadians, had more direct information.

He made a short visit home at the end of July. Pierre was away and Jeanne was able to spend time with her brother. Joseph was clearly on edge, exhausted and worried. He said that it was becoming increasingly difficult for Acadians to move about freely. And there was an increase in privateering activities by the British and the New England colonies.

Joseph had managed to pay a clandestine visit to see his brothers and other relatives in Grand-Pré. "Please don't ask me how I managed this, Jeanne," he said.

"No, Joseph, I won't. But please tell me, how is everyone. Are they safe? Are my step-sisters well, and the twins, how are they? I do think of them."

"Everyone is safe. The girls are all happy. Charles and Anne treat them as if they were their own children. But Charles and Abraham are becoming worried about the situation. And you should hear Uncle Abraham!"

Jeanne was reminded of their visit to Grand-Pré before the fall of Louisbourg, when Joseph had talked to her about their Dugas ancestor as she sat on a mound of hay in Uncle Abraham's barn.

"Did your father-in-law go with you to Grand-Pré?"

"No," said Joseph with a grim smile. "Le Maigre is not going to risk going there now, not after his capture as an Acadian zealot and his terrible imprisonment a few years ago."

"What about you, Joseph? Are you one of these zealots?"

Joseph looked at her intently. He hesitated. "I don't know, Jeanne. It's not that I feel I owe anything to France. I think they have abandoned us. But I am concerned about the Acadians in Nova Scotia and those, like us, outside the British colony. The sad truth is that the Acadians in Nova Scotia just want to live in peace on their farms. They are not a threat to the British, except for a few like my father-in-law who can only cause a bit of mischief.

"Charles and Abraham tell me they hoped that having Hopson as governor would help their cause and they were sorry to see him leave. Apparently he has a problem with his eyes. He's afraid of losing his eyesight and that's why he returned to England. It's too bad he had to go.

"It's obvious that Governor Lawrence's approach is a military one and that he has little sympathy for his Acadian subjects. He calls them 'the French inhabitants,' not 'the Neutrals,' making it clear that he does not consider them citizens anymore. And he is known to have close ties with Governor Shirley of the colony of Massachusetts. Uncle Abraham tells me that bodes no good and I'm sure he's right.

"Anyway, it seems that Governor Lawrence is occupied with administrative matters for now, but the Acadians in Nova Scotia are worried. I know you want to ask me what is going to happen, but the truth is I don't know."

"What about Île Royale? Will it remain French?"

"Ah, Jeanne, that is hard to say. The British would like to have Île Royale, and especially Louisbourg. It would make their shipping lanes secure. The Acadians are not a threat to them in this sense, but they don't seem to realize that. If the British and the French get involved in another war in Europe, then I'm afraid there will be repercussions for us. We're all right for the moment, Jeanne. When I have more news, I will tell you."

—

The end of the season arrived with no great change in the situation. It was a profitable year for both Pierre and Joseph, but a difficult one. Joseph said that everything had gone well, but Le Maigre let drop a few references to what Jeanne believed were scrapes with privateers. Even Pierre had had a run-in with a British ship, and to Jeanne's dismay her husband seemed to be exhilarated by the experience. It was a relief to Jeanne when the snow and ice closed in on them, once again sealing them off from events in the larger world.

Chapter 19

In 1755, the settlers in Port Toulouse awaited the arrival of spring with great anxiety. They were safe for the winter, but as if suspended in space and time. They could not plan for events they could not foresee. The winter passed quietly, the weather was severe. There was less frequent visiting between distant farms. Spring arrived late.

Jeanne was busy with her growing family. Little Marie had had her first birthday in October, and Jeanne's second child arrived in December. They named the new baby boy Pierre Abraham, Pierre for his father and Abraham for all the Abrahams in the Dugas family past and present. He would be known as Pierrot. Despite the busy days in her habitation, Jeanne was deeply worried.

She knew that the political situation was out of her hands. But what if, mon Dieu, Joseph or Pierre were captured or killed on one of their voyages? Or what if it was decided they had to flee once more? She was afraid that Pierre and Joseph would not agree on their destination. Would she be separated from Joseph and his children? She knew her brothers Charles and Abraham in Grand-Pré were planning to go to the Miramichi area, wherever that was, but would they get away safely? And if she and her family followed them, how would they find them? This was a vast country. How would they cope with the children?

The first reports to reach Port Toulouse in the spring were that nothing had changed, but this did not seem to ease the apprehension felt by the Dugas and others. The families went to see the schooners off on the first sailing as usual, but the send-off was somewhat subdued. Jeanne noticed that Martin Sauvage sailed on Joseph's ship, but she did not have a chance to speak with him. Left behind, the families settled into their everyday chores, planting their gardens, tending the farm animals and visiting families on neighbouring farms – and waiting. Jeanne was again with child.

—

Before long they learned that, in the spring, the British had confiscated boats and firearms belonging to the Acadians in Nova Scotia. Early in July, the Acadians had sent a delegation to Halifax to ask for the return of their arms because they needed them to protect their farms against wild animals. The request was refused and the Acadians were told that they must now swear an unqualified oath of allegiance to the English king. The delegates refused and were thrown into the prison sheds on Georges Island in Halifax Harbour. Later in the month a second group of delegates went to Halifax, with the same results. When some Acadians then agreed to sign the unqualified oath, they were now refused. But what did this mean? What would the consequences be?

Joseph was home in early August. He confirmed the reports but did not have much to add to them.

"Does this mean that Charles and Abraham have lost their schooners?" Jeanne asked.

"No," he said.

"Have you seen them, Joseph?"

Joseph hesitated. "I saw Abraham at sea very briefly in May. He said they planned to leave Grand-Pré this summer, but I don't know if they have managed to do so."

"Jeanne," he added, "there's nothing more I can tell you. I know the Acadians in Nova Scotia are very worried. They don't know what these new restrictions mean. There are still some settlers leaving, but fewer than last year because of the new restrictions. And the British redcoats seem to be every-where.

"Some of the older settlers still hope the situation will calm down and that they can continue to live peacefully as before on their farms. But more and more Acadians, both young and old, think differently. And many of them have no easy means of escape."

"What about us, Joseph?"

"I don't know. We'll have to wait and see. Has Pierre been home?"

"Not as much as usual. He is very busy. He thinks that Louisbourg is stockpiling goods in case of war. But he says that the officials at the garrison are not talking openly about this."

"Joseph, did I see Martin Sauvage sail with you in the spring?"

"Yes, Jeanne. Like his uncle Jean, Martin is a very good scout. It's helpful to have him with us. He's able to get good intelligence for us from other Mi'kmaq in various places."

"Has he come back with you?"

"No. We left him at one of the Mi'kmaw encampments and will pick him up there later in the season. Why do you ask?"

"No reason."

"Are you sure?"

"Yes, of course."

Joseph did not return to Port Toulouse again until after his last voyage at the end of the sailing season.

—

Shocking news reached the settlers in Port Toulouse. Acadians in Nova Scotia were being deported. Most of the news they received came from the Grand-Pré area, but it was rumoured that deportations were taking place from other parts of Nova Scotia as well.

On September 2, a proclamation had been issued, ordering all men and boys over the age of ten in Grand-Pré and the neighbouring settlements to present themselves three days later, at the Church of Saint-Charles-des-Mines, to receive a proclamation from the British king. When they did so, they were told that they were to be deported. Their lands, livestock and other effects, except for money and household goods, were forfeited to the British crown. The men and boys were locked in the church to await the transport vessels. They were promised that they would be reunited with their families when they left.

Jeanne was stunned when she heard the news. Her first thought was for her brothers and their families. Had they managed to get away? And where were these people being sent? To France? The procedure of deportation was not unknown. After the fall of Louisbourg in 1745, French settlers and some Acadians had been deported to France. But why would the British authorities do this now, in peacetime? And without any warning?

Jeanne was also worried for Pierre and Joseph. There had been no word from them since early August. Grandfather Coste kept a close watch on incoming ships at the harbour and knowing Jeanne's preoccupation with political news, would pass on any information he received.

In October they heard that British transport ships had finally arrived in Grand-Pré in late September. Two weeks later, fourteen ships laden with Acadians had set sail. The British had not kept their promise to reunite families for the voyage, and the departure had been a disaster, a mad scramble of settlers and their goods and a desperate search for family members. It was also said that as the fourteen ships set sail, the settlers had seen their farms go up in flames as the British deliberately destroyed them behind the deported Acadians.

Jeanne knew that there were bound to be rumours and exaggerations, but even if not all the stories were accurate, the very fact of a deportation not tied to war was unimaginable to her.

Pierre and Joseph arrived home soon after this latest news. Joseph seemed to be in a state of shock. Although he took a cynical view of the British and even the French authorities, he clearly had not considered such an eventuality. He seemed reluctant to discuss the matter with either Jeanne or Pierre.

Pierre pushed his way into the conversation this time. "Joseph, I know you don't usually confide in me," he said, "but this is very serious now and I too need to know what you know and what you think we should do." Joseph seemed startled to hear Pierre speak this way.

"Yes, well, Pierre, I can only tell you the stories I've heard. Acadians are not only being deported from Grand-Pré, but from all different areas in Nova Scotia. They have not been told where they are going, but it seems clear that it is not France. I've heard that they are to be dispersed throughout the British colonies. It's true that families were separated and no effort was made to reunite them for the voyage. And there are reports that some of the ships they boarded were not seaworthy and were overcrowded. Only God knows if all these ships will even reach their destinations.

"Most of the settlers who tried to escape on foot were recaptured by the British militia," he continued, "some shot dead in their tracks. One man who escaped the church in Grand-Pré was captured and his home burned in front of his eyes as a warning to others. The stories go on and on." Joseph shook his head.

"Joseph," Jeanne said, "we hear that one family made it out of Grand-Pré, the Maillets. They are here with Antoinette Martin on her farm. Apparently, they arrived with a wounded man, all of them almost starved to death, and destitute. A second man in their family was shot dead by the redcoats."

"You mean some of them survived? They weren't all killed?" asked Joseph. "That's a miracle."

"Joseph...."

"I know what you're afraid to ask, Jeanne. As far as I know Charles and Abraham and their families managed to get away – and I think before the proclamation. Whether or not they arrived safely in Miramichi I just don't know.

"And you want to know what we should do," he added sadly. "I don't know. I don't know," he repeated. "Certainly, we must stay here for the winter."

—

The disturbing news of the deportation had briefly diverted the attention of the Port Toulouse settlers away from the worry of another war between Britain and France. Jeanne now asked Joseph about this situation.

Joseph sighed and seemed to sag in weariness. "Jeanne," he said, "sometimes I wish I had never started to discuss politics with you."

"Joseph..." she pleaded.

"I don't know, Jeanne. There is no definite news. I just don't know. There was one worrying event. I don't know if you've heard of this, but the British captured Fort du Beausé-jour in June. The French commandant held off the attack for two weeks. He had the help of that black Abbott, LeLoutre, and Joseph Broussard dit Beausoleil. But the French fighters were outnumbered and the fort fell. They say LeLoutre burned down the nearby cathedral to keep it out of the hands of the British. Stupid man. This probably only gave the British another excuse to put the deportation into effect. It's bad news for France, because the fort controlled the Chignecto area, the only overland passage between Louisbourg and Québec in the winter months. But what this means for now, Jeanne, I don't know. I don't know."

Pierre put his arm around Jeanne. "Joseph," he said, "I've thought about all this, and I believe that if you decide to leave Île Royale, Jeanne and I and our children should go with you and your family. I don't know why I can't get an answer from my family as to what they propose to do." Jeanne looked at her husband, surprised.

Joseph nodded to Pierre. "If you're sure." He hesitated. "I can't guarantee you safety, but then I don't think anyone can."

When Jeanne questioned Pierre later, he said that he knew she would prefer to throw in her lot with Joseph. "Thank you, my husband," she said and gratefully laid her head on his shoulder.

—

Again they settled down to a quiet winter. Jeanne liked to think of their secluded little corner of the earth as a safe harbour in the winter months, but now she worried that this winter might be their last one here. Then what? She decided that she could at least take some steps to prepare for whatever they would face. She told Joseph and Pierre of her plans and enlisted Marie Braud's help. Jeanne's plan was that the two families begin to operate as if they were going to flee. They would save some of their dried food supplies for the spring and knit and weave fabric for extra clothing and linens. It would give them a purpose through the long winter months. Jeanne asked Grandfather Coste to make some small wooden cradles to use on the ship for her babies. They all threw themselves into the work.

In mid-November, soon after their plans were put into effect, Jeanne gave birth to her third child. A second girl. Jeanne named her Angélique Anne, for her late sister. She imagined that baby Angélique had her sister's colouring and that she would look like her. "But you'll have to be stronger than my sister," she whispered to the baby. Angélique fussed more than her siblings had, and Jeanne wondered if she sensed her mother's worried state of mind.

Jeanne's main worry was where they would go. At least Pierre had decided they would follow her brother Joseph. But would Joseph choose to follow Charles and Abraham to the Miramichi area, or would he choose some more dangerous path? Jeanne knew very well that he must be having heated discussions with Joseph Leblanc dit Le Maigre during the winter months, but she was not privy to them. Joseph seemed to be reluctant to share his thoughts with her. He said only that most of the settlers in the area of Port Toulouse were planning to leave in the spring, but that he would wait to hear the news the first ships brought before deciding where to go.

Part 3
Flight
to Miramichi

Fleuve Saint-Lauren

Gaspé

Ristigouche La Petite Rochelle

Baie des Chaleurs

Nipisiguit Chipagon

Miramichi Bay and area
Camp de l'Espérance

(ÎLE SAINT-JEAN)
PRINCE EDWA

Richibuctu

(NEW BRUNSWICK)

Shediac

Sainte-Anne (Fredericton) Isthmus of Port
Chignecto Tatama

Jemseg

Rivière Remshic
Saint-Jean

Beaubassin

Cob

Minas Basin

St. Croix Les Mines
(river and island) Baie Française Grand-Pré

Port Royal (NOVA SCOTIA)

Annapolis Basin Annapolis Chez
Halifax

Clare

Saint Mary's Bay

Chapter 20

The first ships of the season in 1756 did not bring confirmation of war between Britain and France, but the looks on the faces of those who brought the news indicated that it was only a matter of time. The settlers knew that events were outside their control.

There was also news of the continuing deportation of Acadians. Jeanne was sick with worry for Charles and Abraham and their families.

"Are they really safe in the Miramichi?" she asked Joseph. "Could they be deported from there?"

"No, Jeanne.... Although I suppose anything is possible at a time like this. But if they are with Boishébert they should be safe."

"I've heard his name," Jeanne said. "Who is he? Is he an Acadian? Not a cousin, I hope," she said wryly.

"No, he's not a cousin." Joseph smiled. "Charles Deschamps de Boishébert was born in Québec. He joined the French troops when he was only fifteen years old and he has spent a lot of his life in our part of the world. He seems to be a man like the first Charles de Saint-Étienne de la Tour. They say he can handle a birch bark canoe as well as any Mi'kmaw, and that he can disguise himself as a farmer or fisherman in order to move around freely and reconnoitre in the woods and at sea."

"But has he fought in any battles here?" Jeanne asked. "Does he understand what is involved?"

"Yes, Jeanne. Boishébert was with the French colonial forces when they captured Port-la-Joye and with the expedition against Annapolis Royal. He took part in the defeat of the British in the Battle of Grand-Pré. When he was commandant of Fort Ménagoache and heard that the British were coming to destroy it, he and his men set fire to the little fort and fled up the river."

"Is he on the side of the Acadians, or of the French?"

"The Acadians. I've heard that he saved more than two hundred Acadians who were being deported aboard the British ship *Pembroke* last fall. I don't know how they managed it, but the Acadians on board overcame the crew and sailed the ship to the mouth of rivière Saint-Jean, where Boishébert took them under his wing and took them up to the Miramichi.

"He's a good man, Jeanne, and he seems to be devoted to the cause of the Acadians."

"Dieu merci. Our brothers would do well to be in his company," she replied.

—

In the spring, Jeanne's and Joseph's families said farewell to families and groups of people leaving the Port Toulouse area ahead of them. There was a sense of things falling apart, a feeling that they were seeing friends and neighbours for the last time. A number were sailing to the Miramichi area, and Jeanne wanted to send a letter on one of the ships to Charles and Abraham, but Joseph said, "Not now, Jeanne." She wondered if it was because he was not sure they were there, but thought it better not to ask.

Late in May, Joseph and his father-in-law discussed their plans with Jeanne and Pierre. Jeanne was dismayed to learn that Joseph Leblanc dit Le Maigre was included in their plans, but tried to hide her feelings. Le Maigre had made arrangements for his family to travel ahead of him to the Miramichi, while he stayed behind to sail on Joseph's schooner.

Joseph decided they would go to Île Saint-Jean. It was under French control and he thought it would be safer than Île Royale. He and Le Maigre believed there was still money to be made in cabotage activities, although they were not sure if France would continue to pay for the transport of Acadians to the island.

"If we find it's not profitable or too dangerous," Joseph said, "we will go on to the Miramichi. Pierre," he added, "you too will be able to carry on this business."

———

The day before they sailed, Martin Sauvage appeared at Jeanne's side when she was having a last walk in her favourite part of the woods surrounding the Dugas settlement.

"I have something for you," he said quietly, taking an object out of its cloth wrapping. "It's to keep watch over you and keep you safe."

Jeanne caught her breath and her eyes lit up. It was a statuette of a woman, a beautiful woman delicately carved in wood, her hands together in prayer, her robe resembling what one would see on a statue of the Blessed Virgin. A delicate fringe was carved at the edge of the garment. Her face had the serenity of a mature woman and her hair hung down her back in a thick plait. She seemed to have the easy grace of a Mi'kmaw woman. And Jeanne saw that although she was praying, her head was not bowed in supplication. It was held high as though facing God on equal terms. It was, of course,

Sainte-Anne. When the Mi'kmaq adopted the Catholic religion, they adopted Jesus's grandmother as their patron saint.

Jeanne looked at Martin through sudden tears. Alarmed at her reaction, he held out a hand to take his gift back. "No. Oh, no," she said. "It's the most beautiful gift I have ever received. Thank you. Oh, thank you, Martin."

They suddenly heard voices and looked at each other guiltily. She quickly wrapped the gift in its cloth and opened her arms to him. He drew her close and held her gently. "I will keep you in my heart forever," he said.

"And you in mine," she whispered. She did not look back. She knew he would disappear into the woods like a ghost. Had he not told her to never worry about him? She smiled, mocking herself. Since when was there someone she did not worry about?

—

They sailed in early June, after bidding a tearful farewell to the Bois family. Jeanne was fond of her in-laws and sorry to leave them. She knew they would worry; but so would she.

Joseph's schooner the *Marie-Josèphe* sailed with four of his children, Marie Braud and Le Maigre. Pierre's schooner, the *Angélique*, carried Jeanne, their three babies, Joseph's oldest daughter, Marguerite (who was now thirteen and could help Jeanne with the babies) and Grandfather Coste. He had asked to accompany them because he favoured his chances with them. Jeanne knew he wanted to help. She would have reason to be grateful for his presence.

The ships were well stocked. They had done everything they could to anticipate their needs. The cradles for the babies were simple boxes with rope handles; they could be secured on the ship and carried when necessary. Although they only had room for strict necessities, Jeanne brought her bundle of special keepsakes, to which was now added the statuette of Sainte-Anne. Jeanne felt a stirring of the same spirit of adventure she had experienced when she sailed to Port Toulouse with Joseph.

Joseph and his father-in-law both knew Île Saint-Jean from their many voyages there. They decided they should avoid the area of Port-de-Joye and its small French garrison. If fighting should occur it would be focused there. They chose a secluded area on the eastern shore, in a cove by a stream of fresh water, and within walking distance of a small farmstead. The first step they took was to visit the farm.

It belonged to Charles Haché and his wife Cécile Arsenault. They had two cows, a few hens, a kitchen garden and three young children. They were happy to have neighbours and more than happy to sell them the foodstuffs they could spare. Like most Acadians they could not subsist on the rations the French government gave them and they did not have the means to farm on a large scale. Joseph would pay them well for their produce.

Jeanne was aware that she and her family had an advantage over many displaced Acadians. They had the two schooners and Joseph had made a great deal of money during his years of cabotage at Louisbourg. Even she and Pierre had managed to put some money aside. They were not destitute, at least not yet.

The men quickly cleared some land by chopping down trees, which they in turn used to build two rustic huts not much more than shelters. Charles Haché came to help them. Jeanne was stricken. Grandfather Coste looked equally distressed. How could they survive a winter in such conditions? Pierre assured his young wife that they would improve the huts before winter set in.

Le Maigre laughed at her discomfort, and Jeanne honestly thought she might at times be capable of killing him. Making the sign of the cross, she asked forgiveness for such thoughts.

A few days later, when they had accommodated themselves somewhat to the living conditions and made arrangements for fresh food from the farm, Joseph and Pierre set sail. They would explore the area and look into the possibilities for some cabotage work. Joseph said he and Pierre also wanted to see what they were up against. Le Maigre offered to stay with the women and children, but Joseph told him very firmly that he was to go with him. "Grandfather Coste is here and he can take charge," he said. It was the first of many instances when Jeanne would be grateful to have Grandfather Coste with them.

She had an additional worry that she had not yet shared with anyone. She was again carrying a child. Most women, she knew, believed they would not get pregnant when they were nursing a baby, but this rule did not seem to apply to her. *Mon Dieu*, she thought, *how can I face giving birth in these circumstances?* She confided in Marie Braud, who was sympathetic and caring, but as helpless as Jeanne.

Joseph and Pierre were away for several days. They returned with stories of the great disarray in the fortunes of the Acadians, both those who had been sent away in British ships and those who had managed to escape. Many of the Acadian refugees who had managed to escape to Île Saint-Jean the previous year to avoid deportation were by now ailing, starving and dispirited, living in crude huts and barely surviving on the rations given to them by the French government.

They also brought back the news that Britain and France had officially declared war on each other yet again.

"What does that mean for us?" Jeanne demanded of her brother.

"Jeanne! Jeanne!" He screamed at her impatiently. She was alarmed. He had never spoken to her this way before. Obviously, his nerves were raw.

"I'm sorry," he apologized. "The war means that we were right to leave Port Toulouse. But I don't know what else it means."

"I hate to say this," he added, "but there are many Acadians who need transport to safety but who don't have the money to pay for it." He had not been able to find out if the French government would still pay for their transport.

"I know. I know," he said, seeing the look on her face. "But what am I to do? Your kind husband here," he said nodding at Pierre, "gave free passage to several Acadians and they robbed him for his kindness."

"It's all right, Jeanne," Pierre said. "I only had a few pennies on me. You would have given them the money if you had been there."

It was good to have the two men back with them, but it did not solve anything. That night, Jeanne told Pierre that they were expecting another child. He did not say anything, but held her close.

—

Joseph, Le Maigre and Pierre continued their cabotage for the rest of the summer. It was not as profitable as in other years. Jeanne suspected that Pierre gave free passage to many more Acadians, but she did not hold it against him. Even Joseph gave in a bit, but he never made a voyage unless there was some kind of payment. It was a haphazard business, not the usual cabotage by contract. Most of the Acadians who now found their way to the Tatamagouche area looking for passage to Île Saint-Jean arrived destitute and desperate. Many lost their lives in their attempt to escape.

In early September, a small shallop anchored near the shore close to their encampment, and several people waded ashore. Grandfather Coste went to meet them and Jeanne insisted on accompanying him. They were Acadians, one man and two women, thin and dirty and dressed in rags.

"Please," one of the women said, "we come in peace. Do you have anything you could spare us? We have hungry children. We need food and money. We will take anything."

Jeanne told Grandfather Coste to stay with them and she went back to get some food. She brought them some fresh meat from small game they had hunted, and vegetables and dried beans bought from the farm. She told them she had no money to give them, but handed them the length of yellow silk that Pierre had given her. She suggested they could sell it to someone.

"Yes. Yes. I know someone who will give us money for this beautiful silk," one of the women said, looking at it greedily. "Are you sure you want to give it to us?"

"Yes. Please take it." It was just the first step in the erosion of her bundle of treasures. She felt a pang of guilt in realizing that the gift from Pierre was the item that she could most easily part with.

—

A week later, in the dead of night, they heard a frightful noise and Jeanne believed they were being attacked by redcoats. But she had no time to think. She nudged Grandfather Coste, who was hard of hearing and still asleep. Then she quickly gathered her three children and Joseph's Marguerite in her arms, and crouched with them at the back of the hut. Grandfather Coste reached for the musket they kept loaded at all times and rushed outside.

Grandfather Coste fired the musket – God knows in what direction – and the wild animal he disturbed ran for its life. He calmly returned to the hut, re-loaded the musket and put it in its usual place, looked to see that Jeanne and the children were not hurt, then lay down and went back to sleep.

Jeanne put her three children back to bed and soothed a terrified Marguerite until she slept. Then she lay down herself, her heart still pounding. She eventually fell asleep, but woke up later in the night with severe cramps. When she woke again in the morning, wet and bloody, she knew she had lost the new baby.

The days following felt unreal. Jeanne was devastated at losing the baby. Although she knew the loss had been caused by the attack in the night – it was, after all, an attack, whether human or animal – she also felt guilty. In an ideal world, she would not have chosen to carry a child at this particular time. Was it wrong for her to feel relief as well as sorrow at the loss? After all, this did mean one less worry in the coming months. She unburdened herself to Marie Braud, who firmly told her that it was God's will, and not Jeanne's doing.

When Jeanne told Grandfather Coste, he in his practical and down-to-earth way told her it was a blessing. "Perhaps," he said, "God realized you have enough to cope with as it is. You already have three healthy children." He awkwardly patted her shoulder.

When Pierre and Joseph returned to the camp at the end of August, Jeanne had come to terms with the loss. But she felt as if a small part of her, or of her innocence, had died. She felt stronger, but it was as if her heart had hardened. It was some comfort to her that Pierre was saddened, but concerned for her health. But when he approached her that night, she turned away from him. "I'm afraid, Pierre," she said. "It's all right, Jeanne," he replied. "I understand." He did not insist.

—

Joseph reported that the flood of Acadian refugees from Nova Scotia was now slowing, and that there was still a lot of confusion as to who should pay for their transport. Those who had money were happy to pay, but there were not many of them.

Le Maigre argued that they could have done better. "You've got to be merciless," he said. "I know there is money to be made, Joseph, if you're tough enough."

Jeanne saw Pierre's mouth tighten.

"That's enough," Joseph said angrily to his father-in-law. "You can't squeeze blood out of a turnip. These people have nothing." They had obviously had this argument before.

Joseph turned to Jeanne and Marie Braud. "Pierre and I have decided that it would be better for all of us to move to Remshic, near Tatamagouche, in Nova Scotia. There is a risk in being in British territory, but it's probably as safe as here. You will be near the port we use as our base, so we will be together for longer periods of time during the season. I agree with Pierre that we should not leave our families alone here so much, even if Grandfather Coste is with you."

"That's right," Pierre said firmly. Jeanne was pleased to see that Joseph had begun to see Pierre as an equal and an ally.

Le Maigre snorted.

"Beau-Père," Joseph said, "I know very well you're worried about going to Nova Scotia because of your reputation there, but I really don't think anyone will be after you in the Tatamagouche area. Things are too much in disarray right now." His father-in-law turned away without replying.

They sailed for Remshic a few days later. Jeanne did not know what awaited them, but she was relieved that they would not be facing winter on Île Saint-Jean.

—

Remshic was a secluded cove compared to the open port of Tatamagouche a few leagues away. But it was crowded with Acadians on the run. At first this annoyed Jeanne, but then she thought, *Mon Dieu, this is what we are too.* Joseph and Pierre had earlier found two small abandoned houses and paid a young man to keep guard over them, but when they arrived the houses had been taken over and the young man was nowhere to be seen. Joseph was furious and determined to throw these people out of the houses. Pierre stayed out of the argument.

Jeanne felt ashamed, embarrassed and frightened. Ashamed because she knew these people were as needy as she. Embarrassed by Joseph's anger and Pierre's silence. Frightened because she did not want to be homeless with her three babies. Her oldest, Marie, was not yet three.

They finally made an arrangement with the squatters to move into one house, leaving the other for the Dugas/Bois group. Jeanne, Marie Braud and all the children would move into the one house and the men would sleep outside – there was not enough room for everyone to sleep inside on the floor. It was not a good beginning.

While Jeanne had felt isolated in their camp in the woods on Île Saint-Jean, here in Remshic she was overwhelmed by the presence of too many people. There were people everywhere, all seeking refuge. The people they had ousted from the house kept a resentful eye on them. Jeanne tried to befriend an elderly woman who was part of the group by offering her some of the turnips and onions they had managed to buy. The woman almost spat at her as she accepted the food without a word of thanks. One of the woman's daughters apologized to Jeanne with tears in her eyes. "Maman is not herself," she said. Jeanne assured her she understood. "Please do not worry about it. I wish I could help you more."

"It's all right. Thank you for this much," the daughter said.

It was barely fall and the weather was grey and cold for that time of the year. Baby Angélique caught a chest cold and then most of the other children caught it. No one complained, but the atmosphere was strained.

One dark rainy day soon after their arrival, Pierre told Jeanne that he thought they should risk going to their home in Port Toulouse for the winter. The British had not yet launched an attack on Louisbourg and the chances were that they would not do so now before spring. Still, when she pressed him for a decision, he seemed doubtful.

"I don't know, Jeanne. I told Joseph how I feel about it, but he did not say anything. I don't know if he agrees or not."

"Ah, Pierre."

"Well, you know your brother," he said and shrugged.

Yes, and I know you too, Jeanne thought to herself, sadly.

They stayed in Remshic through September, and then in early October two things happened that changed Joseph's mind. A group of particularly destitute and determined Acadians tried to force Joseph to take them to Île Saint-Jean and when he refused they tried to steal his schooner. At about the same time, a young man from the area tried to lure Marguerite, Joseph's young daughter, to go for a walk with him in the woods. Pierre was the one who witnessed this and accosted the young man, who refused to let go of Marguerite's arm and insolently told Pierre it was none of his concern. Pierre grabbed him by the scruff of the neck, made him let go of the girl and then punched him in the eye. The young man took off.

It was a frightened Marguerite who told Jeanne the story when she got home. Joseph was horrified at the news. They left for Port Toulouse very soon after. They had been in Rem-shic for almost two months.

—

Their houses in Port Toulouse were still standing, although stripped of anything that could be carried away and used. It didn't matter. It meant coming home. The place that Jeanne had once found basic and lacking the comforts she had been used to in Louisbourg and Grand-Pré now looked wonder-ful. Both Jeanne and Marie Braud wept when they arrived. A stricken Marguerite, who was afraid that the sudden deci-sion to leave had been made on her account, asked them if it was all her fault. "No, Marguerite," Jeanne said, "we're crying because we're happy to be home." Joseph held his daughter in his arms and told her roughly that nothing was her fault.

"Will we stay here now?" Marguerite asked. No one could answer her.

The grown-ups knew that winter would give them a re-spite from enemy attack. They also knew they would have to leave Port Toulouse and Île Royale in the spring, and that finding a place of refuge would become increasingly difficult.

Jeanne was racked with worry from all sides. She worried for the safety of her immediate family and for Joseph and his children and Marie Braud, and for her brothers Charles and Abraham and their families. Secretly, her thoughts were often of Martin Sauvage as well. But she could not let Marie Braud and the children see how anguished she was.

Jeanne knew that Joseph was greatly worried and that he felt responsible for all of them at Port Toulouse. She wondered now if he regretted not following his brothers to Miramichi, but did not want to ask. He continued to answer her ques-tions but did not volunteer any further details.

—

Joseph of course understood the larger course of events. Louisbourg was very important to King Louis XV. It was the French king's key to his possessions in the colonies. France could not afford to lose the fortress, but it had heavy obligations in other parts of the world. Due to the uncertainty that war brings, the cod trade was much diminished and did not cover the expenses of maintaining the fortress and defending it in yet another war. The costs had to be borne by France; the French settlers and the Mi'kmaq could not defend themselves against the British.

The government of France was also facing problems in Louisbourg itself. The fortress was in a state of disrepair. It was becoming more and more difficult to obtain food supplies in the new world. The hope that the Acadians who had migrated to Île Saint-Jean would be able to supply livestock and provisions to Île Royale had not been realized. In fact, Île Royale had to supply the Acadians. Moreover, New France had had several years of bad harvests and had no surplus provisions to send. And there was always the threat that the British would run a blockade against French ships carrying provisions to Louisbourg.

Meanwhile, the rounding up and deportation of neutral Acadians had continued throughout 1756.

Chapter 21

The condition of the three houses on the Dugas land, the scarcity of food, the lack of farm animals – although they did find one abandoned cow – made it difficult to keep up the pretence of living a normal life in Port Toulouse. Jeanne now realized this was something she had come to expect; it was even a source of pride to the Dugas family. As well-to-do Acadians they had lived well and continued to do so even in difficult times, as if it were their due. It was something her family had done in Louisbourg leading up to its first defeat, at Grand-Pré when they visited and then lived with relatives and even, on a lesser scale, at Port Toulouse when she and Joseph had come to settle here after the return of Île Royale to the French. But not this time.

This winter, in addition to the physical discomforts they endured, Jeanne felt as if their homestead was surrounded by a horde of redcoats hovering just on the edge of their little world and ready to pounce on them. The winter itself was long and unpleasant and spring arrived late in 1757. Nearly half a metre of snow fell during the first half of May.

They had decided to use only two of the houses, with Jeanne, Pierre, their children and Grandfather Coste in one, and Joseph, his children, his father-in-law and Marie Braud in the other. They put the precious cow in the third house. Grandfather Coste managed to find some fairly dry cut wood and they used it sparingly with green wood for heating and cooking. Joseph and Pierre fished and hunted small animals. A real hardship was that they had no flour, until one day Joseph, after one of his scouting trips, appeared with a full barrel of it, unspoiled. "Don't ask me," he warned.

They had shelter, they had food, they had each other, and Le Maigre kept his distance from Jeanne, for which she was grateful. Now she knew what it was to be grateful, and to pray seriously to God to keep them safe. First on her list were Marie, Pierrot and Angélique. Pierre and Grandfather Coste. Joseph, his children and Marie Braud. Even Le Maigre – that he not do anything rash that might bring disaster upon them. She included all her other relatives in one basket. At the very end of her prayer she shyly asked le bon Dieu to protect Martin Sauvage.

Jeanne did not let her children out of her sight. Marie was now a quiet but alert three-year-old, Pierrot a lively handful at two, and Angélique had just turned one. Jeanne worried that her youngest might have the weak health of her own sister, Angélique. For hours each day, while she worked in the house, Jeanne carried Angélique next to her heart in a sling, trying to impart to her some of her own strength. Joseph's children and Marie Braud spent most of their days at Jeanne's house and there was a sense of security in being together in one place. They sang the old songs to the children to keep them amused and Grandfather Coste carved toys for them.

There were now very few other inhabitants in the Port Toulouse area and no one close by. When sailing conditions became impossible late in the fall, the two families were truly isolated. Jeanne found her thoughts divided between worry about the dangers posed by the political situation and worry about their chances for survival.

She had returned her bundle of treasures to the built-in chest where it had been stored before. One long winter evening after the others were asleep, she unpacked the bundle and allowed herself the luxury of letting each item bring her memories of happier times. The blue silk gown and the necklace Joseph had given her, the portrait of her in the gown as the innocent young girl she had once been, the beautiful embroidered shawl she had made at the convent, her books and Martin's gift of the statuette of Sainte-Anne. She remembered the piece of yellow silk that Pierre had given her, but told herself that it had not been part of her original bundle of treasures anyway and that she had given it away for a good cause.

She caressed the statuette. The wood felt silky to the touch. And Sainte-Anne's stance, not defiant, but facing God as an equal, seemed to ask Jeanne to be courageous. As she wanted to be.

———

Until now, Jeanne had believed that keeping an eye on those around her, and having her brother Joseph with them would protect her. She realized now that she had been looking at things as if through a fog, certain that those around her could and would cope with whatever misfortune befell them. Even when they had left Port Toulouse the previous spring, she had still thought that life would go back to some form of normalcy for Acadians. She remembered how she had foolishly thought of their departure as another adventure.

Well, their adventure on Île Saint-Jean and in Remshic had removed the curtain of fog from her eyes and brought home to her the brutal reality of their situation. She knew now, without Joseph having to tell her in so many words, that he expected the French to lose the battle for Louisbourg. There was nothing he or anyone else could do to prevent this, and the only question was how they were to survive and to escape deportation. She remembered her Maman's fears for Joseph and, over and above all their problems, her heart ached for the destruction of his hopes and dreams.

Jeanne understood, with great clarity, that it was the isolation from the greater family circle, not knowing where Charles and Abraham and other Dugas and Bois family members were, that truly signalled the end of her former way of life.

—

They both knew they had to leave Port Toulouse in the spring, but Joseph and Le Maigre disagreed on how late they could leave. To Jeanne's frustration, Pierre was again shut out of the discussions. Joseph had been in search of news as soon as travel along the coast became possible and had spoken with the few Mi'kmaq who were returning to their summer camp by the sea. Most of the Mi'kmaw families had stayed at their winter camps, judging they would be safer if fighting broke out. The general intelligence was that three squadrons of ships and frigates from France had safely arrived at Louisbourg and that as of early June there was still no sign of the arrival of British ships. When Jeanne asked if Joseph had seen Martin, he answered a curt "No."

They delayed their departure until mid-June, sailing once again to Remshic, but this year without a shipload of supplies. After what Jeanne considered to be a very silly argument, Joseph brought the cow with him on his ship. The alternative was to slaughter her for the meat, but they had no salt and would have lost most of it. Jeanne breathed a sigh of relief. Little Pierrot liked the cow. He had named her "Moomoo."

Joseph and Le Maigre had hoped to find some cabotage activity in Remshic and Tatamagouche, but they were disappointed. Many Acadians had been deported, and no doubt any who remained were in hiding. The village itself was half abandoned.

They found shelter in two empty houses, but it was more difficult to find food than it had been the previous year. Jeanne was grateful to have the cow and insisted that they use another abandoned house to shelter it.

"That's not necessary in the middle of summer, Jeanne!" Joseph was angry, though she suspected his anger was not really aimed at her. Jeanne knew she was being difficult, but Moomoo was part of their family group and Jeanne thought she too should be made as comfortable as possible. It might be folly on her part, but she was determined to protect those still in her life – even Moomoo.

Pierre came to her rescue. "We'll find Moomoo a house," he said, and he did.

Joseph was clearly disturbed. Aside from the lack of cabotage activities and the danger of capture and deportation, there was also the fear of being attacked at sea by privateers, either French or British. It was difficult to escape them if they came after you, because they were armed and often larger than their prey. Of course, Le Maigre played the "I told you so" game with Joseph.

"If I had my own schooner," he kept bragging, "I'm telling you I'd be out there with the best of the privateers."

"Just ignore him, Jeanne," said Joseph.

They had been in Remshic for about a month when they heard from a Mi'kmaw scout that there were redcoats heading their way looking for any remaining Acadians. Le Maigre questioned this intelligence, but Joseph trusted the Mi'kmaw even if he did not know him personally and insisted that they leave Remshic immediately. They gathered their meagre belongings and were ready to leave when Pierrot cried out, "Moomoo! Moomoo!"

Joseph stopped in his tracks and looked around in frustration, then marched to the house to fetch the cow. Jeanne, Marie Braud and the others looked at each other ready to burst into laughter but not daring to. As Joseph walked past them leading the cow, he said, "Oh, go ahead, laugh." Soon they were all laughing, with little Pierrot running behind the cow happily shouting, "Moomoo, Moomoo."

—

They sailed to Île Saint-Jean and found the place where they had built the past summer, but their huts had been torn down. They walked to the Charles Haché farm and found it abandoned. There were no farm animals and no crops had been planted. Joseph decided they should stay there until he could get some information on the situation. "At least Moomoo has a home," he said with a wry smile. Pierre, with the help of Grandfather Coste, anchored his schooner in a cove nearby where it would not be seen from the sea, while Joseph and Le Maigre went to scout out the area.

This part of the island was isolated at the best of times, but there now seemed to be a deeper strangeness in its character – an emptiness, as if the land itself were abandoned. They anchored along the coast closer to Port-de-Joye and walked tentatively through the bush. Suddenly, three men stepped out of the brush before them, one of them Charles Haché, whom they greeted like an old friend.

Charles told them that when news had spread around the island in the spring that Louisbourg might fall again, the settlers expected the worst. Those who had the means to do so had left. The others, like him, had not even planted crops. In any event, most of the settlers had lost their crops for the past two years. There had been almost no help from the French government. The settlers had been given guns and ammunition and told to send their women and children into the woods at any sign of the redcoats approaching. "A few of us men come out to scout certain areas every few days. We are thinking of returning to our houses for the winter months if the war has not been won, but...."

Joseph quickly assured him that they would have left the area before then. "I would like to be able to give you some good news," he said, "but I don't think there is any. We will see you again before we leave, and if there is any urgent news we will get it to you. Be brave, my friend," Joseph said, and he slipped Charles some coins as he shook hands with him. "Our compliments to Cécile." Charles nodded his head in agreement.

Joseph and Le Maigre returned to the Haché farm, Joseph wondering how much to tell Jeanne and Pierre and Grandfather Coste.

"I have never lied to you, Jeanne," he said to her, "even if I have sometimes not told you the whole truth.

"The situation here is not good. We might be in more danger than I expected. Still, we have an advantage over other settlers because we have the schooners and we still have some money."

—

In mid-September, Joseph learned that the British redcoats had indeed made one last sweep of the Tatamagouche and Remshic areas looking for stray Acadians. He also knew it was inevitable that if the colony of Île Royale fell to the British, the Acadians on both Île Royale and Île Saint-Jean would be deported. Would they be safer in Remshic after this latest deportation? Joseph reasoned that the redcoats would not be coming back to the area soon or at least before next spring.

They had to wait until early October to sail, because in the third week of September they were hit by the most violent storm ever seen in the area. They anchored their two schooners in the most sheltered cove they could find, and barricaded the Haché farmhouse as best they could. But the wind and rain and hail that pounded them for days were truly frightening. *As if le bon Dieu has not sent us enough grief*, Jeanne thought. The children were afraid and only Pierre could comfort them. *At least my husband is a good father and I should be grateful for that*, Jeanne told herself. And their schooners were not damaged. What was it Maman had told Jeanne when she was little? Learn to be grateful for the really important things. But Jeanne thought that if she had to listen to Grandfather Coste sing "Sur le pont d'Avignon" and "Le chant de l'alouette" to the children one more time she would scream.

Joseph tried to find Charles Haché after the storm abated, but could not locate him or any of the other settlers. Had they gone farther into the woods? Were they still alive? There was no way of knowing. And they had to leave soon.

When they arrived in Remshic they found the small village now completely deserted, except for eight decaying bodies abandoned there. One had been thrown halfway up a tree. The men buried them and Jeanne led the family in a prayer for the repose of their souls.

—

They survived the winter there – they did not eat as well as usual, but they ate. Jeanne was not displeased to see Le Maigre lose some weight, and she did not apologize to God for her thoughts. Jeanne and Pierrot, each for different reasons, regretted the fact that Moomoo had been left on Île Saint-Jean.

They had all agreed to leave her there for the Haché family should they come back to their farm for the winter.

—

Louisbourg had survived another year, due to the late arrival of the British ships to the waters off Île Royale, the strength of the three French squadrons that protected the fortress and the violent storm that hit in September causing damage to both French and British warships. The British had been prevented from fulfilling their plan to capture the fortress and then attack Québec. They retreated, but there were rumours that eight of their warships remained anchored at Halifax for the winter.

Chapter 22

During the winter of 1758 they tried to keep up a sense of normalcy for the sake of the children, but it was difficult. Joseph's older children wanted to know why their lives had changed. Marguerite was sixteen, Anne thirteen, the twins Ti-Jos (Joseph) and Mimi (Marie) were ten and baby Françoise was eight. Marguerite was a bit like her Aunt Jeanne, her father said to her one day, because she wanted to know everything. "The two of you will drive me out of my mind," he told them jokingly.

Jeanne's children were too young yet to understand. But Marie, the oldest, seemed to sense the tension and worry of the grown-ups. She became quiet and withdrawn and stayed at her mother's side. It made Jeanne's heart ache to see her that way. Marie Braud never complained, but she seemed to become paler and more wraith-like each day.

Le Maigre looked worried, and was unusually quiet, which made him less of a thorn in Jeanne's side. Grandfather Coste spent hours telling stories to the children about the wonderful Acadia he had known and of his early life there in better times. In the evenings, even if their hearts were heavy, they sang the old songs to the children to put them to sleep.

Pierre searched the deserted village and surrounding area for anything they could use or eat, such as dry wood for fire or vegetables left behind in abandoned kitchen gardens, and he had fished and hunted with the others. Jeanne knew that her husband was there for all of them like a solid and loyal bulwark. But it was on Joseph's shoulders that their safety and survival depended and Jeanne knew this weighed heavily on her brother.

—

The problem in the spring, as always, was the need for news. In the spring of 1758 the need was urgent and the means to obtain it difficult. But although they were isolated for their own protection, they needed some contact in order to know what was happening. A few stray Acadian men had gone through the Remshic area early in the spring, but they had no news to share with them. Joseph had told several men that if they should come across some Mi'kmaq, and especially a scout named Jean Sauvage, to please tell him that Joseph Dugas and his family were in the Remshic area. They promised, but weeks went by with no response.

Joseph made a few careful excursions on his schooner, but did not dare go very far in case he might be seen by enemy ships or privateers.

Jeanne understood their options very well. Stay in Remshic and eventually be killed or deported by the redcoats? Leave and be captured at sea? If they did sail from Remshic, where would they go? Surely to try to escape to the Miramichi at this point in time would be folly? She had visions of their small schooners surrounded by huge British warships. These days she was praying as much to her Maman as to le bon Dieu, feeling that perhaps Maman would understand her concern for her family better than He.

Joseph kept an eye on the sea. In mid-May he spied a Mi'kmaw canoe approaching shore. He ran out to show himself and greet them. To his relief and joy he recognized his old friend Jean Sauvage. His nephew Martin was with him.

"I am happy to see you are still here," said Jean. "I heard about you and your family only a few days ago."

Joseph brought the men to his house, where everyone gathered. After everyone had greeted each other, Joseph looked around helplessly at Marie Braud and Jeanne. They should be offering their friends refreshments but they had so little to give. Martin noticed this, and said, "No. We will bring you some food and supplies soon. You have done well to survive here." Jeanne tried not to look hungrily at Martin and she imagined that he was doing the same.

Jean Sauvage reported to Joseph that five French ships, plus a squadron of five war vessels, had arrived safely at Louisbourg in the month of April, carrying supplies. Jean guessed they had been able to stock enough food and militia matériel to last for a long siege. It was believed that other ships had been captured or lost at sea, and Governor Drucour did not know if he could expect more ships.

Attempts had been made to repair the fortifications of Louisbourg, and the French had built a line of coastal field posts at the Baie de Gabarus to the south, as well as at the rivière Miré to the north. They hoped to prevent the British from landing along the coast near the Miré to attack the fortress from the rear as they had done in 1745. And of course the French had their warships safely in Louisbourg Harbour.

But since the beginning of May, the eight British warships that had spent the winter at Halifax had been sailing back and forth across the entrance to Louisbourg Harbour. There was no way of knowing when the full force of British warships would arrive.

Governor Drucour had sent an appeal to Charles Deschamps de Boishébert, who was in Québec, and he expected Boishébert to arrive at Louisbourg with a force of perhaps as many as eight hundred to twelve hundred irregulars – fishermen and settlers who were part-time soldiers – native warriors and Acadian volunteers. Jean Sauvage did not expect such a large number. He knew there would be fewer Mi'kmaw warriors because they had not been impressed with the war effort the previous summer.

"Jean, what should we do?" Joseph asked his friend.

"I believe you should return to Port Toulouse while you wait for developments," Jean replied. "Boishébert is expected to stop there when he arrives and perhaps he will have news for you."

Le Maigre came suddenly to life. "Joseph," he said, "we could join Boishébert's militia."

Jeanne and Marie Braud looked at each other with the same thought – *Ah, non.*

"Jeanne. Marie," Joseph appealed to them. "Don't start worrying. We don't know what's going to happen. I think Jean's advice is good."

"Yes," said Jean. "There are other Acadians and Mi'kmaq at Port Toulouse waiting out the events and you will be as safe there as anywhere else."

"And Jeanne," argued Pierre, "Boishébert may be able to help us reach the Miramichi."

Jean Sauvage and Martin returned a few days later with food supplies, and escorted the Dugas and Bois families and their two schooners safely to Port Toulouse, sailing along the north shore of Nova Scotia, keeping close to the coastline.

Their habitations were still standing and empty, but Joseph warned that they should live there as they had in Remshic, ready to leave at any time. A few days after their arrival, they heard that two caboteurs and their schooners, as well as two merchant ships, had been captured by British ships not far off the coast. And there were many rumours about the activities of the privateers. This had a sobering effect on Joseph and Le Maigre.

There were some twenty or so Acadian volunteers waiting for Boishébert at Port Toulouse, most of them men who had fled from Île Saint-Jean, as well as a dozen Mi'kmaw warriors. This ragtag group of Acadians and Mi'kmaq, like the Dugas and Bois families, were pinning their hopes on the arrival of Boishébert. Jeanne sensed they were rather uneasy at having two families with children among them.

Jean Sauvage and Martin, with three or four other warriors, went to and from Port Toulouse on scouting expeditions. Whenever they returned, Martin always came to their habitation to make sure they were safe, usually bringing food with him. Jeanne was reminded of the berries he had brought her in the past. Was it only six years ago? It seemed like a lifetime.

Chapter 23

Charles Deschamps de Boishébert arrived at Port Toulouse at the end of June, weary and short of provisions and men. He had left Québec with three vessels on May 8, bringing a few compagnies franches officers and cadets, and seventy volunteers. Due to bad weather it had taken him a month to reach the Miramichi, where he added seventy Acadian militia and sixty Mi'kmaw warriors to his forces. He now had a total force of fewer than three hundred men, nowhere near the twelve hundred Governor Drucour expected.

All the men awaiting Boishébert came to greet him. When Joseph introduced himself, Boishébert said, "Ah, Joseph Dugas. I have a letter for you or your sister Jeanne Bois from your brother Charles."

"Ahh—" Jeanne cried out and clutched a hand to her heart.

Joseph handed the letter to his sister. "Here," he said softly. "You read it."

She felt tears coming, but did not want to cry until she knew what news the letter held. Good or bad? She unsealed it very carefully with trembling hands, and read it silently.

My dear brother and sister,
I hope with all my heart that this letter will reach at least
one of you and find you in good health. We want you to
know that we, Charles and Abraham and our wives and
children are all living, thank the good Lord. And also our
stepsisters and the twins. We are worried about Jeanne and
Pierre and your children, and Joseph, your children and
Marie Braud. It would ease our hearts to know that you
are alive and well. And it would bring us great joy if you
could join us. We pray for you and ask the good Lord to
keep you. We all send you our love.
Your brother Charles Dugas

She held the letter against her heart. Then she broke down in loud sobs of relief.

"Jeanne! What is it?" Joseph put his arm around her and pleaded with her to tell him. Finally, her sobs eased. "I'm sorry," she said, "I'm so sorry, but I couldn't help it. They are fine." She read them the letter out loud.

"Ah, Dieu merci!" exclaimed Joseph for all of them.

"He mentioned me, too," Marie Braud whispered with a smile.

—

Boishébert cast a look at the Acadian volunteers and the dozen Mi'kmaq waiting for him at Port Toulouse. It was obvious he was not impressed. Le Maigre spoke up. "Sir, you have three more volunteers. Myself, Joseph Dugas and Pierre Bois, Jeanne's husband."

Boishébert gave a half-smile. "You have ships?"

"We have two schooners, Joseph's *Marie-Josèphe*, 32 tons, and Pierre's *Angélique*, 24 tons. They've been used for cabotage only. We have no arms."

"I can take you on my ships," Boishébert said.

The wave of joy that Charles's letter had brought to Jeanne now vanished. Her stomach muscles tensed at the thought of Joseph and Pierre joining the militia.

Boishébert was silent for some minutes. He seemed worried and distracted.

"Well," he said finally, "we face a difficult situation. There was a letter waiting here for me from Governor Drucour. The Governor expects me to make my way to Louisbourg. But considering the most recent intelligence, this seems to me to be impossible. Drucour's letter also tells me that the cache of ammunition and food that was hidden near the rivière Miré has been broken into by some Mi'kmaq." Boishébert was tired from his seven-week trip from Québec, worried about his lack of men and already short of provisions.

"The British, I understand, have landed at the Baie de Gabarus," he continued. "So I am heading for the Miré where there should be some supplies remaining. By the way," he gave a wry smile. "Drucour's letter also included the Order of Saint-Louis, which the king has awarded me. A high honour indeed. Perhaps the king and Drucour believe it will enable me to do miracles."

A number of the men started to congratulate him, but Boishébert calmed them down. "There's no time for that now."

Boishébert looked around at the men. "I'll take all of you who wish to join me to the Miré. Dugas, if you want to follow with your two schooners, I'll take you three men on my ships as part of my irregular force when we arrive there. I'm sure you understand that I cannot guarantee the safety of your families, although I'll do as much as I can to protect them."

"Agreed." Joseph gave his hand to Boishébert, followed by Le Maigre and Pierre.

Jeanne was torn. She had heard of Boishébert's exploits and especially of his sheltering Acadians in the Miramichi.

She believed him to be a honourable man, but his objective was to fight a war. She knew very well that the Dugas and Bois families were only very small bits of flotsam caught in the wake of his much larger ships.

Jeanne asked her brother if Jean Sauvage and Martin would be with the other Mi'kmaw warriors on Boishébert's ships. He told her no, that they were more valuable to the war effort as scouts.

"Is that very dangerous for them?"

"Yes, Jeanne, it is very dangerous, but they are very skilled at what they do. I expect we will see them at the Miré."

—

Boishébert arrived at the rivière Miré on July 1, followed by Joseph's and Pierre's schooners. Boishébert anchored his ships off the Miré beach. Guided by Grandfather Coste, who knew the area well, Joseph and Pierre found a small cove a bit farther inland in which to anchor their boats.

Jeanne knew that the area had farmland and that a few Frenchmen and Acadians had settled there to plant grains and vegetables and raise cattle. But even though grains, except for wheat, grew well in the area, they had not managed to create any substantial farms. The cattle-raising business had been more successful, but it had never been able to supply all the needs of Louisbourg. If Jeanne expected the kind of bucolic farmland she had seen in Grand-Pré, she was sadly disappointed.

The first thing she noticed was the field posts along the shore, manned by the French militia. The Miré area was a battlefield shared with civilians. The farmers had tried to isolate themselves, hoping to stay out of the battle. There were poor French and Acadian civilians who had fled the fortress hoping to find a safe refuge, and others who had come from

Port Toulouse. There were also a number of Mi'kmaw warriors and their families. All these people were scattered over a fairly large area, but of course there was not enough shelter for everyone. It seemed to Jeanne that there were a great many women wandering around who seemed to be alone.

"Don't go near them, Jeanne," Joseph cautioned. "They are camp followers, both English and French. Some are fairly decent women, others would cut your throat for a loaf of bread. Don't try to befriend them, do you hear me?"

"Yes, Joseph." *But, mon Dieu*, she thought, *they are human beings.*

"We'll be able to get food here," Joseph continued, "but we are going to live on the schooners. Even if we could find shelters, we are safer aboard the ships."

Grandfather Coste, who had made a removable mast for Pierre's ship, suggested that they pull the *Angélique* ashore, remove the mast, and turn the boat over. They could sleep under it and have some shelter.

Joseph shook his head. "No. If we are attacked, either by the enemy or a thief, it will take us too long to try to get away." Pierre nodded his agreement.

Joseph turned to Jeanne. He held her arm and looked into her eyes. He wanted her full attention. "My sister," he said seriously, "if something should happen to us when we are with Boishébert, Grandfather Coste is to take all of you in my ship and sail for the Miramichi."

"Yes, Joseph, I understand." Jeanne tried to look brave, even as she felt an icy grip on her heart. Marie Braud looked even paler than usual and her lips trembled. But she said nothing.

Chapter 24

To his dismay, Boishébert found that there was very little left of the caches of food and munitions meant for the French troops. He lost no time in setting up raids against the British lines, but with little success. Joseph, Le Maigre and Pierre joined the irregulars. Pierre was proud of his role as a cannoneer on one of the ships. They made a few unsuccessful raids by sea, and then Boishébert set up harassing raids on land. But although they wounded a few men and captured one or two prisoners, their raids were little more than a nuisance to the enemy.

Left on their own with Grandfather Coste and the children, Jeanne and Marie Braud were like lost sheep in a place they did not understand. It seemed that everyone around them was to be treated as suspect. They slept on the schooners and if the three men were away the two women and Grandfather Coste took turns staying awake and keeping watch during the night. Jeanne and Grandfather Coste went out each day in the field in search of supplies and food. They brought Marguerite with them one time, and that was a mistake. Young and pretty, Marguerite was met with ribald remarks from men and women alike. She was terrified. At night they would often hear the noise of drunken merrymaking from members of the militia and the camp followers.

Grandfather Coste suggested that they not worry their three men with these reports and Jeanne agreed. But she was worried about Grandfather Coste. She had been aware for some time now that he was short of breath when he walked for any distance and was not his usual self.

—

At dusk on still another evening when the men were away, Jeanne heard a slight noise coming from the side of the schooner. She shushed the children and went to check. It was Martin Sauvage, in a small canoe.

"Jeanne, don't be afraid," he whispered. "I want to talk to you. Can you come with me for a little while?"

She did not hesitate. "Yes, I'll just tell Grandfather."

She came back, put the rope ladder over the side of the schooner, and with Martin's help climbed down to his canoe. He put a finger to his lips, settled her in the canoe facing him, and slowly and silently paddled a short distance along the shore and stopped when the canoe nudged against a fallen tree. She broke the silence.

"Martin, the men are with Boishébert," she whispered.

"Yes, I know," he said.

"Ah, mon Dieu, are you here to give me some bad news?"

"No, no, Jeanne. I wanted to see for myself that you are safe. This is a bad place to be."

"Yes, but we don't have any choice. Do you know what is happening? Please tell me, Martin." She extended a hand to touch him, then drew it back. He took her hand and held it in both of his. His hands were strong and calloused yet held hers very gently.

"Jeanne, do you truly understand what is happening? The battle for Louisbourg is almost over and the British are winning. Then they will capture Québec. You will be deported or you will be a fugitive in your own land. I do not know what will happen to my people. We have nowhere to go, so we will remain, but I don't know how will we survive. I think many of us will die. We won't be able to share this land with the British the way we have with the Acadians and the French. Does Joseph have a plan for you?"

"Yes, we hope to go to the Miramichi with Boishébert," said Jeanne. "Charles and Abraham are there. We had a letter from them."

"I know. And Boishébert is a good man, but he won't be able to protect the Acadians in the Miramichi for much longer. The British have already destroyed Acadian settlements on the Baie Française and along the rivière Saint-Jean. Now they are attacking settlements in the Chipoudi and the Petitcodiac and the Memramcook areas. If they continue they will surely reach the Miramichi and eventually destroy all your areas of refuge. There will be nothing left for you but to accept deportation."

"But we don't want to go, Martin. This is our home."

"I know," he said with a small smile. "You Acadians are almost as attached to this land as we are. And you have only been here a very short time compared to us."

Jeanne could not help but think back to when she was a child and thought she understood so much. Now the world she knew seemed to be turned upside down. It was all changed, and it was her enemy. She hesitated before speaking. She could not put her thoughts into words, but sensed he would understand.

"You know, I always feel safer when you are with me, Martin," she said with a sad smile.

"And I always feel that I'm a better man when I am with you," he said. "I'll take you back to the ship. I have to go now.

I've brought some food. I even found some berries for you," he said with a smile.

"Ah, Martin." Tears rolled down her cheeks. "Thank you. Especially for the berries," she smiled through her tears.

He paddled back to the schooner as silently as he had left it. Grandfather Coste was anxiously waiting. Jeanne climbed back into the schooner with the gifts. No one said a word.

—

It wasn't long before Boishébert's men became tired and discouraged. When a number of them fell ill, there were many desertions. The militia from Port Toulouse and the remaining Mi'kmaw warriors were among the first to leave. Soon Boishébert had only about a hundred and forty men left. He decided his mission was doomed and he sent a letter to Governor Drucour to advise him of this. He told his remaining men that he was planning to return to the Miramichi at the first good opportunity and that he would take anyone who wanted to leave with him.

Spirits were low among Boishébert's remaining troops and in those who hoped to follow him to safety. It was as if there was a slowing down of time – the days seemed longer and the movements of men slower and more cumbersome. Boishébert led a few more sorties against the British siege posts, but the attempts seemed half-hearted, as if his troops were only going through the motions. Even Joseph seemed ashamed of their efforts, and Le Maigre was very angry at the idea of giving up.

Jeanne overheard Le Maigre mutter that maybe the rumours about Boishébert being there only to trade and line his own pockets were true. But Joseph angrily defended him.

"You know very well that Boishébert is a good man. And you know very well that the King awarded him the Cross of

Saint-Louis this past summer." This was indeed a high honour and the French king bestowed it only on the most deserving.

—

For the Bois and Dugas families living on their schooners anchored in an inlet of the rivière Miré, the tension and worry increased. It became more dangerous and difficult to forage for food. Jeanne kept an eye on Grandfather Coste. She could tell his health was failing, even as he denied it. And Jeanne knew by Joseph's demeanour that he was very worried and on edge. She knew him so well, she could read him as easily as she did her bibliothèque bleu books. She had placed her family's safety totally in his hands and she began to wonder if this was perhaps unfair of her. Had she asked too much of him?

In any event, they did not have very long to wait. On the afternoon of July 27, Jean Sauvage, his nephew Martin and several other Mi'kmaw scouts arrived with the news that Louisbourg had fallen to the British. The great fortress had come to an ignoble end, forced to surrender without being accorded the traditional honours of war. The entire garrison were to be taken as prisoners. Nothing had been said about the fate of the inhabitants of Île Royale or Île Saint-Jean, but it was assumed that the British intended to deport them.

Chapter 25

The next few days passed by in a flurry of preparations. Boishébert wanted to leave before the British came to clear out the Miré area.

Joseph gathered his two families together and surprised them with the announcement that he was sailing to Québec to try to obtain Lettres de Marques from the French governor to authorize him and others to operate as privateers.

Jeanne gasped and quickly covered her mouth with her hand.

"I am sailing there with my father-in-law on my schooner," he continued. "Jeanne, the rest of you will sail to the Miramichi on the *Angélique* with Pierre and Grandfather Coste."

Ti-Jos said he wanted to go to Québec with his father, but Joseph instinctively said, "No." Then he hesitated, looked pensively at his twelve-year-old son, and relented. Perhaps he remembered growing up with his own father. "Very well," he said, "you can come with us, Ti-Jos. We could use another man on board."

It was obvious that Ti-Jos was thrilled from head to toe, but the decision sent a chill down Jeanne's spine.

"We'll be fine, Jeanne," said her husband. "Grandfather will be with us and we'll be sailing with Boishébert's group."

"I know, Pierre, I know." Marie Braud was deathly pale. Jeanne put a comforting arm around her. Joseph sailed a day before Boishébert and his ships.

As they saw Joseph off on the *Marie-Josèphe*, Ti-Jos looked happy and proud to be sailing with his father, but to Jeanne he was tiny and vulnerable. *Mon bon Dieu*, she prayed silently, *please protect them, and all of us*. Grandfather Coste, who was standing behind her, patted her awkwardly on the back.

Later in the day, when Pierre and Grandfather Coste were away from the schooner looking for more supplies for their trip, Martin Sauvage came for a last visit. He was carrying a child, a little boy who looked to be about Pierrot's age. The child's big brown eyes watched everything around him in silence and he clung to Martin so fiercely that his little fingers were white.

"Martin, who is he?"

"I don't know. He has been with us for a few days now and I have not been able to find his parents. I think they must have been killed. I tried to find a family to take him. Acadians are usually good that way, but two families yelled at me that he is a Huguenot and that they want nothing to do with him." He paused. "There are times when I find it difficult to understand your god, Jeanne."

"Ah, Martin, there are times I do not understand Him myself."

"We can keep him with us, but I believe he would be safer with his own people. Our situation is very uncertain, as you know."

"Are you asking us to take him, Martin?"

"I am asking *you* to take him, Jeanne," he replied, looking into her eyes.

She held her arms out to the boy. "What is his name?"

"I don't know. He's old enough to speak, but he has not said a word. And I have no way of knowing what he's been through to make him like this." The boy buried his face in Martin's neck and held on to him even more tightly, ignoring Jeanne's arms.

Martin murmured to him softly and started to gently pry his little fingers open.

"Viens, mon petit," Jeanne said. Finally, he lifted his head and blinked and looked first at Jeanne and then at Martin and back to Jeanne. Then with a last glance at Martin, he gave up and went into Jeanne's arms, clinging to her just as fiercely. Jeanne held him and crooned to him.

Marie, who had been holding on to her mother's apron, went to Martin. "Uncle Martin," she said, "I'll help Maman to take care of him and I'll be good to him. I promise."

Martin put his hand on her head. "Thank you, Marie. One day you are going to be wonderful woman and a wonderful maman. Just like your Maman. Jeanne ..." he began.

"I understand, Martin. Thank you for coming to me."

"The boy was barefoot when we found him and we've given him some moccasins. I've brought some extra ones that should fit your children. You may need them later on. And I've brought you some dried meat and beans."

"Thank you. Will I see you again, Martin?" She was on the verge of tears.

"Yes. Yes. I'll do my best to keep track of you. And if things ... get very bad and you need me, tell any Mi'kmaw and I will come to you." He put his arms gently around her and the boy and then silently melted away.

—

They sailed the next day. Boishébert's ships carried his remaining troops and a number of homeless and destitute Acadians.

One of his ships called at Port Toulouse to pick up others. It was a bold effort on Boishébert's part. Jeanne could see why Joseph admired this man. But she was fearful. There were two sides to their adventure. One, the excitement of fleeing from the defeated Île Royale; the other, the very real worry as to what awaited them in the Miramichi.

The *Angélique* was crowded as never before. As well as Jeanne's family and Grandfather Coste, their schooner was carrying Marie Braud and four of Joseph's children, the little orphan, and a stray man who had joined them at the last minute. He told them his name was Michel Benoist and that he was an Acadian who had lived on Île Royale most of his life. Grandfather Coste thought he remembered his family and said they should take him.

The new man turned out to be a godsend and Jeanne wondered if perhaps God did sometimes really care. As Pierre soon realized, his grandfather was no longer capable of pulling his weight on the schooner, and Michel stepped in. Grandfather Coste was able to save face by acting as the ship's captain and overseer.

Jeanne felt herself pulled in ten directions at once. The most immediate and urgent tug came from the little orphan, who would not leave her side. Marie and the other children tried to amuse him, but he ignored them. Pierre told Jeanne to put him down and let him fend for himself, but she couldn't.

When she had first explained him to the others and said he was probably a Huguenot, no one had objected. But Pierrot was frustrated by not knowing what to call him, and said, "Hu ... no ... guenot ..." then, triumphantly, "Nono!" He loved words like that and for better or worse that became the orphan's name. Nono ate if Jeanne fed him and Nono slept if Jeanne was beside him. It was awkward during the day. The younger children were used to spending their time on board ship tied by a rope to the mast so that they would not wander too close to the side of the ship and to protect them in rough seas. But Nono reacted so violently to that idea that they did not insist. So Jeanne and Nono were inseparable. But if all went well, the voyage should only take a few days and perhaps little Nono would be less fearful on land.

A bigger worry was the news that Michel Benoist brought with him. Grandfather Coste asked him if he was familiar with their destination, the Miramichi. His reply made Jeanne wish that Grandfather had not asked.

Michel explained that in the years leading up the deportation in 1755, a number of Acadian families who were worried about the political situation had sought refuge on the rivière Saint-Jean, Michel and his young family among them. They had settled along the river in family groups, surviving by cultivating small farms and by hunting and fishing. In 1754, the French had a small fort, Ménagoèche, established at the mouth of the river, with Boishébert as commandant.

The following year, after defeating Fort Beauséjour, the British had sent troops to capture Ménagoèche. Aware of the plans, Boishébert had burned the fort before the British arrived and taken several hundred refugees up the northeast coast to make his headquarters on an island in the Baie de Miramichi. It was considered a good spot for hunting and fishing and brought new hope to the Acadian families. They named the island Camp de l'Espérance. Michel paused and looked off into the distance.

"Well," he continued in a voice rough with emotion, "it wasn't. A camp of hope, that is. The government of Nouvelle France was in charge of supplying Boishébert, his men and the refugees with food and support, but corrupt officials stole the money set aside to buy provisions, and the people at the camp were left to fend for themselves.

"During the winter of 1757, hundreds of Acadians died at Camp de l'Espérance, from starvation or from smallpox. All our children died. Those of us adults who survived ate anything we could find, even at the end our deerskin boots. Finally, we had nothing; we lay on the ground, with Boishébert, his officers and soldiers and waited for death.

"Then in early May," Michel continued, "we were rescued from death's door when a ship made its way through the ice and brought us provisions. The hardiest of us survived." He paused and shook his head, looking off into the expanse of ocean.

"I was not going to tell you," he said, "because I feel so guilty for surviving. I left my wife and two sons buried there. So now you know."

"Ah, mon Dieu," Jeanne cried out, "you poor man." She hesitated. "But you're going back?"

"There is nowhere else to go," he said softly.

"But ... but I think my brothers were there at the time.... And we've had a letter from them. It seems they are alive and well."

"I'm sorry, Jeanne. I shouldn't have told you all this. I assure you, it's quite possible that your brothers were not at Camp de l'Espérance at the time this happened. They could have been hiding in the area. Some of the Acadians took to the woods and some of them took refuge with the Mi'kmaq. Please don't worry, Jeanne, I am sure that is what happened." She nodded, but how not to worry?

"I'm told that Camp de l'Espérance has now become a place of transit for refugees escaping Louisbourg and Île Saint-Jean on their way to Ristigouche Poste or Québec. So I'm not sure just where Boishébert is taking us," he added.

Jeanne wondered if this meant that they might not find themselves in the same place as Charles and Abraham after all.

Chapter 26

The *Angélique* was one of the last ships in their group to reach land at Miramichi. Jeanne wondered if they would land on Boishébert's island or on the mainland. Pierre said they would follow the other ships. As their schooner came closer to the shore of the island there was great confusion with several ships arriving at once, but they could see there were shallops waiting to take them ashore. Pierre dropped anchor and they all stood facing the shore waiting for a shallop to reach them.

Jeanne held Nono in one arm and Angélique in the other. Marie held on to her mother's apron. Pierrot, afraid of nothing, was standing at the end of his rope as close to the side of the ship as he could get. Jeanne could hear shouting from the shore and from other ships, but on the *Angélique* there was complete silence, as if they were all frozen in place.

Jeanne glanced over at Grandfather Coste, who was as pale as death, Pierre standing anxiously beside him. Marguerite stood with her sisters and with an arm around the trembling Marie Braud. Michel Benoist faced the shore like the others, but his eyes seemed unfocused, as if he did not want to see.

Their silence was broken by the gentle bump of a shallop against the side of the *Angélique*. A rough voice shouted up to them: "Who are you?"

Pierre shouted back. "Dugas ... and Bois. Dugas and Bois."

The man turned and shouted the names back and the names were picked up and shouted closer and closer to the shore.

"Dugas! Bois!"

"Dugas! Bois!"

"Dugas! Bois!"

Suddenly, Jeanne saw a man jumping up and down on the shore and waving his arms wildly. Mon Dieu! Could it be Charles or Abraham? He was too far away for her to see what he looked like, but Jeanne said to everyone, "Wave to that man! Wave to that man!" She put Angélique down so she could wave and suddenly Nono squirmed from her grasp her and got down, waving with the others.

The women and children were quickly put in the shallop, which would come back for the men. Jeanne looked anxiously at Grandfather Coste. He was sitting on an upended cask and Pierre was holding him. Pierre lifted his hand to Jeanne as if to say, "It's all right. Go."

Jeanne kept her eyes on the man on the shore. He was watching them and tracking their shallop to see where it would land. Finally, they were close enough and she could see that it was indeed her brother Charles. She tried to shout to him but her throat wouldn't make the sound. Instead, she forced a smile and waved and he smiled and waved back.

None of them on the shallop had spoken yet. The two men who rowed the boat had kept silent too, as if they sensed something strange about their travellers. Strong hands helped Charles and the rowers to haul the shallop onto the sand.

Charles went to Jeanne first. "Ah, Jeanne!" He picked her up out of the shallop but as he started to carry her further up the beach Nono started to wail. Jeanne found her voice. "Ah, mon Dieu, that little boy thinks you're taking me away from him. Put me down, Charles, I'll have to take him with me." She ran back and took Nono with her, while the men disembarked the others. Charles was holding out his arms to them, as if he would take them all in his embrace.

"Where are the men?" he asked.

"The shallop is going back for them. There is my husband, Pierre Bois, his grandfather Jean Coste, and another Acadian, Michel Benoist."

"And Joseph?" Charles looked stricken.

"No, no, Charles, he's well. At least we think he is. Joseph has gone to Québec hoping to pick up Lettres de Marques from the French Governor so he can be a privateer."

Charles put back his head and gave a bark of laughter. "He hasn't changed, has he? Did he go by himself?"

"No, his father-in-law, Joseph Leblanc dit Le Maigre, is with him. And Joseph took his twelve-year-old son Ti-Jos with him too. And you're right, Joseph has not changed."

"And the rest of you are safe! Tell me who everyone is, Jeanne. It's so long since I have seen any of you." So Jeanne introduced him to everyone. Joseph's children, Marguerite, Anne, Mimi and Françoise. "Mimi is Ti-Jos's twin. Remember? They were born in Grand-Pré. And Marie Braud, who came to Port Toulouse with us from Grand-Pré."

"Yes, of course, I remember."

"And these are my children, Marie, Pierrot and Angélique. And this is the new member of our family, Nono. We've adopted him."

Charles hugged and kissed all of them. Jeanne wondered how Nono would react. But Nono, having watched all this, decided he had no choice and accepted the show of affection.

In the meantime, the shallop was on its way back with the men.

Jeanne told Charles how she was worried about Grandfather Coste. She knew he was ill, but did not know what was wrong.

"We will take care of him, Jeanne." Charles put a strong arm around her shoulders as they watched the shallop approach. *He radiates strength and purpose*, Jeanne thought. He seemed to have a stronger sense of himself than she remembered. Perhaps it's because of all the hardships he's gone through, she thought.

When the men got off the shallop, Pierre and Michel had to help Grandfather Coste. They walked on either side of him and half carried him along. He was deathly pale and seemed unaware of his surroundings. They sat him down on a rough bench someone brought forward.

"Charles, this is my husband, Pierre Bois," Jeanne said.

Charles shook his hand and gave him a rough hug. "I am so glad to meet you."

"And I to meet you, sir," Pierre said.

"Not sir, just Charles."

"This is Michel Benoist, an Acadian from Port Toulouse," Pierre said. "And my grandfather, Jean Coste, who is ill. I don't know how much farther he can go on. Are we to stay here?"

"No. Now that Louisbourg has fallen, we are fairly certain that the British forces will attack the Miramichi area and especially Camp de l'Espérance island. Most of the refugees who came here and survived," he added, "have either gone on to Québec or to La Petite Rochelle at the Ristigouche Poste. That is where we are going, and my plan was to lead you there today if you arrived early. If your grandfather is not well enough to travel we can wait here for a few days.

"Is your grandfather the Jean Coste who is well known in Acadia as an expert shipbuilder and brilliant navigator?"

"Yes," Pierre said proudly. "And we were fortunate to have him travel with us these last few years."

"He's a wonderful man," Jeanne added.

Michel Benoist had been keeping an eye on Grandfather Coste as they spoke. Now he called to Pierre.

Grandfather Coste had fallen off the bench and Michel was trying to raise him up. Pierre hurried over. They laid him down on the sand. He opened his eyes to look at Pierre and tried to speak.

"It's all right, Grandpère. Just rest. We're right here with you." Oh dear God, he prayed silently, don't let him think we would abandon him.

They took Grandfather Coste to an empty rough habitation and laid him on a paillasse. Boishébert came to look at him, but shook his head when he left. "I have seen other men in his condition," he said. "Even if we had a surgeon I don't think he would be able to help him." Pierre stayed with him.

In the meantime, Charles was making arrangements for all of them to eat and sleep on Boishébert's island.

When Jeanne brought some food to Pierre late in the afternoon, she found him sitting quietly on the floor, head down and eyes closed, beside the body of his Grandfather Coste.

"Ah, Pierre." Tears filled her eyes. "I am so sorry. When did it happen?"

"Just a little while ago. I wanted to stay with him to say goodbye."

She knelt beside Grandfather and put her hand on his forehead. His skin was still warm. "Thank you, Grandfather, for all your love and help," she whispered. "I will go and tell the others, Pierre."

Charles and Boishébert accompanied her back to the hut.

"Pierre, I'm very sorry for your loss and that it happened to him so far from his home," Charles said.

"Thank you, Charles. But I think Grandfather would consider that he had a good death. He was still on his beloved sea, helping others, and he died an Acadian."

"You are quite right, young Pierre Bois. Your grandfather was a noble Acadian," said Boishébert. "If you agree we will bury him on this island with the other Acadian patriots. There is a good chance that Abbé Manach will be here tomorrow and, if so, your grandfather will have a proper Christian burial."

"Thank you, sir."

"If you agree, Pierre, we will hold a veillée for him during the night," Charles said.

"I think Grandfather would like that."

Abbé Jean Manach arrived the next morning and officiated at Grandfather Coste's funeral and burial at the cemetery on the eastern end of Boishébert's island. The area was barren, with not even one tree to break the bleakness of that point of land in the sea. The graves were marked with simple wooden crosses, each bearing a name. Jeanne wondered how long it would be before the names were erased by wind and rain and the crosses simply disappeared.

After the ritual Michel Benoist approached Abbé Manach and asked him if he would say a prayer at his wife and sons' gravesides. The Bois and Dugas families accompanied him and joined in the prayers.

As they walked away from the cemetery, Jeanne remarked on the cold wind from the gulf that was blowing over the graves.

"It's all right, Jeanne. Grandpère would like that." Pierre was fighting back tears.

She put an arm around him and walked closely with him.

"I don't think you understand, Jeanne. You have all your relatives. Grandpère was my only contact with my family."

Mon Dieu! It was true. She should have seen this before and been more concerned for her husband. Now all she could think to say was, "Pierre, you know my family is your family."

They sailed for La Petite Rochelle in the Baie des Chaleurs the same day. The death of Grandfather Coste and their hurried departure after his burial cast a sombre pall on them as they set sail.

Chapter 27

The *Angélique* followed Charles's schooner, the *Saint-Charles*, up the coast, into the Baie des Chaleurs, and then into the mouth of the Ristigouche River. Jeanne did not know what awaited them there. There had been very little time to talk with Charles, after Grandfather Coste's death and burial. Charles had simply said, "We will explain everything when we reach the Ristigouche."

It was almost ten years since Jeanne had left Grand-Pré with Joseph to go to Port Toulouse! Would Charles's and Abraham's children remember her? There would be some she had not yet met. And would there be a difficulty with providing her group with food and lodging? What were the family's circumstances here?

Ah, mon Dieu, she thought suddenly, *where is Nono?* Wrapped up in her worries, she had forgotten about him for a moment. She turned to look for him and there was Marie, a rope in each hand – Pierrot at the end of one, Nono at the other – marching up and down the deck.

"It's all right, Maman, I'm going to tie them to the mast in a moment." Marie had a big smile on her face and so did Pierrot and Nono. Wonder of wonders!

Jeanne had to laugh. "Thank you, Marie, my big girl."

—

It was late in the day when they docked at a makeshift wharf on the north side of the Ristigouche River, at Pointe-à-Bourdon. They stood on the deck of the schooner, each holding a small bundle of personal effects, half apprehensive and half joyful at arriving. Charles had docked before them and now came to help them disembark.

"Look, Jeanne," he said, pointing to a large group of people standing a short distance from the wharf.

"Ah, mon Dieu! All the family!"

"Yes, there was a ship in ahead of us and the news arrived before we did." He laughed happily.

As they walked down the wharf the family ran to meet them. Charles's wife, Anne, Abraham's wife, Marguerite, and all their children. And Jeanne's stepsisters, Marie and Louise, and the twins, Charlotte and Anne, the four of them now grown women. They all had tears running down their cheeks as they laughed and hugged and kissed. Jeanne proudly presented Pierre and her children and Nono – and Joseph's children of course, and Marie Braud and Michel Benoist. Abraham waited for a while, then said, "Hey, Jeanne, you have another brother here too." They all laughed and wiped away tears again, as Abraham hugged his sister.

Charles said, "In case you have not heard yet, Joseph is not here. Our intrepid brother has gone to Québec to get some Lettres de Marques so he can become a privateer! His son Ti-Jos is with him. Mimi's twin."

Jeanne finally caught her breath. "Charles, will you be able to cope with all of us?"

"Jeanne, we are family. We are Acadian. We are not as wealthy as we were in Grand-Pré, but we have survived so far and – well, see how many of us there are!" He and Abraham each had eight children. "And now with you and Joseph and your families here we are complete. Let us pray that Joseph returns. I, for one, will bet on it. *Sacré,* he's got nerve!"

"Jeanne," said Anne, "you must be exhausted. Come, you and Pierre and your children and Michel Benoist will come to our house. Abraham and Marguerite will take Joseph's children and Marie Braud with them. Tomorrow we'll get together and catch up on our stories." Anne had a meal ready for them – a feast it seemed to Jeanne.

"Mon Dieu! You have bread!" she exclaimed.

"Yes, there are two outdoor ovens at the fort that we use," Anne replied. "And we get flour and other provisions from the fort, as long as the ships can get through to the poste."

—

The Ristigouche Poste at Pointe-à-Bourdon was a simple wooden fort surrounded by a stockade, with barracks, stores for supplies, a forge and several other buildings. The fortifications included four batteries of cannons strategically placed up and down the river. La Petite Rochelle was a straggling temporary settlement of Acadian refugees nestled along the river on both sides of the poste. It extended from Pointe-à-la-Mission, where there was an encampment of Mi'kmaw families, to an area west of Pointe-à-Bourdon. The Acadians lived in simple habitations hastily erected without foundations; most of them had a small kitchen garden. Many of the refugees had become fishermen and a number of them became privateers.

The commandant at Ristigouche Poste was Jean-François Bourdon de Dombourg. Bourdon, born in France, had arrived in Louisbourg at the age of thirteen. Discovering he had a facility for languages, he had become an interpreter for the Mi'kmaq. In 1758 he had been ordered to join Boishébert's group of irregular forces. He was now in charge of a handful of troops and more than a thousand refugees.

The storekeeper at the fort, in charge of distributing provisions to the forces and the Acadian refugees, was Pierre du Calvet. He was a recent arrival from France who had come to try his luck in the new world. Intending to become a trader, he had the misfortune to lose the merchandise he brought with him in a shipwreck. Unable to set up business for himself, he'd accepted the position of storekeeper at Ristigouche Poste.

—

It was a long time since Jeanne had been able to lean on an older woman. Anne, Charles's wife, took her under her wing. She noticed Jeanne's tenseness and her air of worry and apprehension. In fact, she thought Jeanne looked old beyond her years. The morning after their arrival, when Anne sympathetically asked her what was wrong, Jeanne broke down in tears. Anne took her in her arms.

"It's nothing," Jeanne sobbed. "It's nothing and everything." Then she poured out her heart to Anne. Her life at Port Toulouse, her marriage to Pierre, giving birth to Marie when she was alone (she did not mention Martin), the moves from Port Toulouse to Île Saint-Jean, to Remshic, to Port Toulouse, to Remshic, to Île Saint-Jean, to Remshic, to Port Toulouse, to the Miré and now to the Ristigouche. How they stayed in each place sometimes for only a few months at a time, in rough lean-tos, in abandoned houses or even on the schooner. And living in fear. Always the fear and the uncertainty.

"Please, Anne, don't think that I regret following my brother Joseph to Port Toulouse. I really don't."

"I wouldn't blame you if you did, Jeanne." Anne sighed. "You're not telling me everything, are you?"

"Isn't that enough?" asked Jeanne. She attempted a smile. She could not bring herself to mention her disappointment in Pierre, or her attachment – that is what she would call it – to Martin, her resentment of Le Maigre and what she saw as his influence on Joseph. She could not explain her silly attachment to her bundle of treasures, the relics from her childhood that she could not abandon.

"Ah, Anne, you must think me so ... so weak."

"Non, ma pauvre Jeanne, you are a very strong woman. You are trying to take everyone's burden on your shoulders and there has been no one to help you. Well, now there is someone to help you. You must eat well and let yourself sleep without worry. We will help you with the children and with Joseph's family. We don't know what tomorrow is going to bring, but the healthier and stronger we are, the better our chances to survive."

—

The next few days at La Petite Rochelle were spent talking – catching up with each other's lives and telling stories.

Jeanne begged Charles to tell her honestly what they could expect there. "We have been wandering from one place to another, moving almost every few months for three years now," she said. "Are we safe here, Charles? We've been told that Boishébert leads a band of Acadian resisters in this area. Doesn't that worry you? What does he hope to accomplish?"

"Ah, Jeanne, you're still the little girl who sat quietly in Uncle Abraham's house at Grand-Pré and listened to the men talking about politics, aren't you?" He smiled fondly.

"Well, this is much more serious," he continued, more soberly. "It is true that Boishébert is the leader of a group of irregular forces – Acadian refugees, Mi'kmaw warriors and a few French forces. They call themselves resisters. They run a kind of little war against British ships and troops, when they can find them. They haven't a chance of inflicting any real damage to them yet. But yes, it worries me.

"What most of us want, is to go on living here, peacefully, in this little corner of the world. Surely the English could spare us this much land. We are not a threat to anyone. We live in peace with the Mi'kmaq. We just want to create a home for our children.

"Jeanne," he continued, "I simply don't know what is going to happen. But I believe you are in the safest place you can be right now."

She turned to look at her husband. Pierre nodded reassuringly. "He's right, Jeanne."

Charles stood and rubbed his hands. She would come to learn that this meant he had a plan. "People come and go, in this place," he said. "When someone leaves, that means an empty house. Come, there's a good chance there is one available for you."

Charles took them to register their family at the fort, and then to see the house. It was simple, but it had a hearth and some basic furniture. It would be available in a week or so. And it was just a short walking distance from Charles and Anne's home. It would be fine. Jeanne's spirits lifted.

—

Early in September, Joseph arrived, with a handful of Lettres de Marques and enough small cannons, muskets, knives and hatchets to arm several schooners. Ti-Jos brought back stories of the trip that kept the other children enthralled for days.

Joseph and Le Maigre also brought news. The British had started to deport Acadians from Île Saint-Jean, but it was taking a long time because they found many more than they had expected. In the meantime, a good number of Acadians were making their way to the island's north shore hoping to be picked up by French schooners and taken to the Baie des Chaleurs or Québec. Le Maigre quickly found sympathizers at La Petite Rochelle, and he sailed with them for Île Saint-Jean. Jeanne was not sorry to see the back of him.

—

The deportations from Île Saint-Jean were only part of a general campaign by the British to remove any remaining Acadian resisters from the shores of the golfe du Saint-Laurent before the planned British attack on Québec the following year. During the fall of 1758, the British attacked the Acadian and Mi'kmaw settlements at the Miramichi. They found only a few starving refugees, but they burned down all the settlements regardless. They also made devastating attacks on Acadian settlements along the Saint-Jean, the Chépoudi and the Petitcodiac rivers. In some instances, the Acadian refugees had time to disappear into the forests before the British troops arrived. When they were found, they were killed and scalped – even the women and children. In all cases, their settlements, livestock and crops were decimated. This resulted in a shortage of food supplies for the general area and an increase in the number of refugees making their way to La Petite Rochelle.

At this point in time, privateering became a matter of survival for the large number of refugees at La Petite Rochelle. Only by raiding British supply ships loaded with provisions could the settlement hope to feed its inhabitants.

Joseph Dugas and his brothers Charles and Abraham were among the most successful privateers. Among the others were men who were also resistance leaders, including Joseph Broussard dit Beausoleil, Joseph and Pierre Gautier and, of course, Joseph Leblanc dit Le Maigre. Within a few months they had captured seventeen British supply ships. That the privateers were able to capture the much bigger British ships was an example of great seamanship and daring. And it was a big thorn in the side of Charles Lawrence, the British governor of Nova Scotia.

Joseph operated from both Richibuctu and La Petite Rochelle. Pierre served as a member of the crew on Joseph's schooner. As well as the *Marie-Josèphe*, Joseph co-owned another ship with Le Maigre.

Le Maigre had returned from one of his voyages transporting refugees with his wife Anne and son Paul on board. Several of his children had died and they did not know the whereabouts of the others. Anne was a small, wizened woman now – a shadow of the woman Jeanne had known at Port Toulouse. Sadly, she died soon after her arrival at La Petite Rochelle.

Chapter 28

Life at La Petite Rochelle was a welcome respite for Jeanne. She soon responded to her sister-in-law Anne's attentions, good food and rest. Jeanne had her family and they had a home. As soon as they were settled, she asked Pierre to bring her special bundle from the ship.

Joseph's family too had settled into their own house. Michel Benoist went to stay with them until Joseph's return and then decided to stay on. Even Marie Braud looked better, with a bit of colour in her cheeks. Little Nono was slowly turning into a normal child. But if, heaven forbid, he took his cues from Pierrot he would get to be a handful too! Jeanne was grateful, but there was always a strong current of worry and fear. How long would they be safe in this new refuge?

The two families gratefully slipped into the rhythm of village life. It was good for the children to be able to run and play in the fields with their cousins. They interacted with other refugee families and the Mi'kmaw families who came regularly to the Fort.

One day Anne asked Jeanne to accompany her to a neighbour's house where an Acadian woman, Marie Landry, was due to give birth. When they arrived, Anne quickly realized that it was a breach birth and that the woman's life was in danger. She asked the husband to try to get Maman Mimikej, the Mi'kmaw midwife, to come and help. Luckily, she was at the fort with her husband and she arrived quickly.

She came in and rushed to Marie's side, speaking a little French. "You'll be all right. All right now, Maman," she said. She brought with her an aura of calmness and serenity to replace the fear and anxiety that had filled the little room. She very gently and patiently manipulated and massaged the frightened woman and the baby, while Anne and Jeanne each held one of the mother's hands, until the baby entered the world head first as he was meant to. Tears were running down Jeanne's cheeks.

"Why do you cry?" asked Maman Mimikej.

"Ah, it's because my first child was brought into the world by a wonderful woman like you," she said. "In Port Toulouse – Potlotok."

"You have feeling for people who suffer. You would make a good sage-femme. I will teach you."

"Yes, please. Please." Jeanne was grateful. This was a way she could help. It was the beginning of a close friendship between her and Maman Mimikej.

Whenever a refugee woman asked for the midwife, Jeanne went along to assist. Soon Jeanne found that if Maman Mimikej did not arrive in time, she was able to cope on her own. After her first delivery, when Maman arrived late and saw the baby and the ecstatic look on Jeanne's face, she laughed happily.

"You are ready now," she said.

Jeanne already knew something about the use of herbs and plants as medicine, but Maman Mimikej taught her how to use many more, such as sweet grass, white spruce, alder, cherry tree, flagroot and golden thread. Eventually, Jeanne dared to ask her if she knew any Mi'kmaq from the Potlotok area, such as Jean Sauvage and his nephew Martin.

Maman Mimikej said that she did know Jean Sauvage and his nephew, who sometimes came to the area as scouts. "I will tell them that you asked about them," she said.

—

In the spring of 1759, Jeanne and Pierre, like most of the other refugees, planted a small kitchen garden beside their house. The children helped, if you could consider Pierrot and Nono's running around as help, and Jeanne thought that it was among their happiest times since they had first left Port Toulouse in 1756. In June they celebrated a marriage.

A romance had blossomed between Marie Braud and Michel Benoist. This must explain why Marie looked less peaked and timid, thought Jeanne. Jeanne was so happy for her she cried when she heard the news. And how wonderful for Michel, who looked like a new man. The Dugas families decided to make it the most wonderful wedding celebration they could manage in the circumstances. Marie Braud insisted she did not want a fuss made, but Jeanne, Anne and Marguerite told her she was going to have as much fuss as they could muster.

When Marie told Jeanne that she did not have a decent dress to get married in, Jeanne thought of the blue silk gown in her bundle of treasures. She would never wear it again. When she brought it out and showed it to her sisters-in-law and Marie, they gasped. Marie Braud was overwhelmed. Jeanne insisted she try it on. There was no hoop underskirt, but that would have been too much under the circumstances anyway.

On a beautiful day in June, with Abbé Manach officiating, Marie Braud and Michel Benoist were joined in matrimony in a field near Jeanne's house. The shy bride was beautiful, the groom overwhelmed. The families feasted on meagre rations and made music and danced as if they were back in the Acadia of their youth. For a few brief stolen hours their fears and worries were pushed aside. The celebration lasted until darkness fell. It was as if no one wanted to go back to the real world.

Chapter 29

The Dugas brothers and Pierre Bois were now officially members of Boishébert's militia. Charles and Joseph were majors, Abraham was a captain and Pierre was a lieutenant.

In the spring of 1759 Boishébert and a small force of Acadian volunteers sailed for Québec to help in its defence. Boishébert's force fought in the battle of the Plains of Abraham in which Québec was defeated. He was back at Ristigouche Poste in September, with orders from the French commandant to return in the spring with a larger force of Acadian volunteers for the defence of Montréal. But Boishébert realized that the defeat of Québec had sapped the spirit of the Acadian resistance.

Only two French controlled settlements remained: Montréal and La Petite Rochelle.

The Dugas brothers and Pierre Bois had not accompanied Boishébert to Québec, but they and their fellow privateers had kept up their activities. In the summer they captured thirty British prisoners during their raids and held them at the poste. Du Calvet, the storekeeper, wanted to return them to the British at Halifax, a step strongly opposed by the leaders of the Acadian resistance and by the Mi'kmaq, who knew very well that this would mean revealing the location of La Petite Rochelle to the British. But du Calvet insisted and eventually had his way.

Jeanne had never seen Joseph so angry. "This is madness. What is du Calvet trying to do to us?" he cried. Joseph had resumed his habit of confiding in Jeanne and she was grateful. It was much less worrying to know what was happening and to have some idea of the possible consequences. But Joseph had no encouraging or comforting words to offer her.

The fall of Québec was ominous for the refugees. They understood very well that there was very little chance that Montréal could successfully resist the British. And, even if the refugees managed to remain where they were, how long could they survive their vagabond life without any support from the French? Even the hardened leaders of the Acadian resistance acknowledged that their situation was hopeless. Many of the refugees in the camps scattered along the North Shore were already facing starvation, and the meagre food supplies at La Petite Rochelle were drying up. Privateering could not go on indefinitely.

Chapter 30

In the fall of 1759, the British became preoccupied with the fate of the ragtag but determined Acadian resisters in the Miramichi and on the Baie des Chaleurs. In October, General Edward Whitmore, the British governor at Louisbourg, issued a proclamation offering the Acadian refugees an olive branch. He advised them that if they surrendered peaceably, he was "ordered by His Majesty to assure you that you will continue in the enjoyment of all your goods, the freedom of your property, with the full exercise of your religion." Should they refuse the offer, they would face "a war without mercy: no quarter, no prisoners, no ransom."

Although the refugees tended to mistrust the offer, many felt they had no choice if they were to survive. The three missionaries in the area, the Abbés Maillard, Manach and Charles Germain, encouraged them to submit. Abbé Maillard was also trying to arrange a truce with the British for the Mi'kmaq.

In November, several delegations of Acadians went to surrender to the British at Fort Cumberland, taken there by resistance leaders such as Joseph Broussard dit Beausoleil and his brother Alexandre, and by Jean Basque and Simon Martin. Several hundred Acadians living in camps along the north shore of the Baie des Chaleurs also surrendered at Fort Cumberland, and at the British fort at the mouth of the rivière Saint-Jean.

A number of Acadian leaders remained opposed to accepting the offer from the British, among them Joseph Dugas, his brothers and Joseph Leblanc dit Le Maigre. Boishébert, still at his base at La Petite Rochelle, was furious when he heard of the surrenders. Boishébert, Joseph Dugas and Bourdon, the commandant at the Ristigouche Poste, all wrote angry letters of protest to Abbé Manach, questioning his patriotism. The Abbé at first argued that the refugees should accommodate themselves to the situation in which they found themselves, but later he too would have doubts about the word of the British.

Whether or not General Whitmore had acted in good faith, Charles Lawrence and his council made the decision that the Acadians who surrendered would be deported to England. The deportations began in late winter and the news soon reached the remaining refugees on the North Shore. The Acadian leaders vowed to continue their resistance and made their way to La Petite Rochelle to join Boishébert.

Chapter 31

The winter of 1759-1760 at La Petite Rochelle held feelings of dread and worry and helplessness Jeanne knew so well. It seemed to her a repeat of their winter in Grand-Pré waiting for the first fall of Louisbourg in 1745, of their last winter in Port Toulouse after the deportation of 1755, and of the two winters they spent in hiding, in fear of the second fall of Louisbourg in 1758. Once again, they were waiting to see what news spring would bring. Her respite in La Petite Rochelle had been brief.

Early in the spring, Pierre du Calvet, the fort's storekeeper, quietly boarded a ship bound for Montréal. He commented to one of the militiamen that there were almost no provisions to allocate anyway. Boishébert sailed for Montréal soon after.

—

In mid-May, three French merchant ships, the *Machault*, the *Bienfaisant* and the *Marquis de Malauze*, sailed into the Baie des Chaleurs, armed with supplies and munitions destined for Québec and Montréal. The leader of the expedition, François-Gabriel d'Angeac, aware that British naval ships had out-sailed them and lay in wait ahead, led the French ships to shelter at the mouth of the rivière Ristigouche. They landed at Pointe-à-la-Batterie and made camp. When d'Angeac saw that the Acadians in La Petite Rochelle and the surrounding area were near starvation, he agreed to give them some of his provisions.

This brought some badly needed relief, but the leaders of the Acadian resistance knew that the presence of the French ships would draw the attention of the British. The Dugas brothers, other resistance leaders and the Mi'kmaq held many discussions. Jeanne was reminded of the heated arguments at the de la Tour home in Louisbourg and at the Dugas homes in Grand-Pré, but now she had a greater worry. She knew that if fighting broke out in the Baie des Chaleurs, her three brothers and Pierre would be in the thick of it because they were now in the militia. This would not be a war fought somewhere else.

The Mi'kmaq soon heard rumours that a British fleet was on its way. Indeed, Captain John "Mad Jack" Byron had left Louisbourg at the head of three large British warships with orders to destroy the French force in the Baie des Chaleurs.

There were roughly 1,500 people in the La Petite Rochelle area at this time, including the militia, Acadian refugees and their families, and the Mi'kmaq and their families. There was general agreement that in the event of a battle the women and children should flee to the forest, taking with them as much sustenance as they could.

"Mon Dieu, Joseph," asked Jeanne, "how are we to survive?"

He looked back at her, blankly. She felt herself flushing in embarrassment. How could she ask him such a question. She wasn't a child anymore. "I'm sorry, Joseph," she said.

He just shook his head sadly.

—

The British warships arrived in late June and the naval confrontation began on July 3, when the British made their way toward the main channel of the Ristigouche. The battle saw several changes in fortune, but only lasted five days. On July 8, the French commandant scuttled two of his ships, the *Machault* and the *Bienfaisant*, to prevent the British from taking their valuable cargos. The third ship, the *Marquis-de-Malauze*, held British prisoners and was spared. The British later destroyed it, along with about twenty other vessels, mainly Acadian schooners, shallops and small privateers. The French manpower under d'Angeac, which consisted of 200 Troupes de la marine, 300 Acadians, and 250 Mi'kmaq, were helpless against the much larger British force.

—

The arrival of the British warships had spread fear in the hearts of the Acadian women in La Petite Rochelle. Some fled immediately, others waited to see what would happen. A few were too sick or weak to move, and simply resigned themselves to wait for death. Jeanne thought something must be done to help those who could not help themselves. Charles's wife Anne told her kindly but firmly that they could only hope to save themselves. "This may seem hardhearted to you," she said, "but please listen to me."

Anne and Marguerite gathered together the Dugas and Bois women and children and they quietly slipped into the woods the day after the naval battle started. At the last minute, Anne and Jeanne went looking for Marie Braud, who refused to leave. Her husband Michel was on duty at the fort and she would not leave him. Anne tried to reason with her. "We are all leaving our husbands here," she said. "You must come with us, Marie." But Marie refused. Jeanne wanted to stay with Marie, but Anne grabbed her by the arm and said firmly, "No."

They left, each adult clutching a bundle. The older children carried younger siblings.

Anne had obviously thought this through, perhaps with her husband Charles. "We will follow a southeast path," she said, "and do our best to stay hidden. We will try to reach the settlement of Nipisiguit. Our husbands will come to look for us there."

Jeanne could only look at her, stunned by her sister-in-law's strength. She followed.

Chapter 32

It was a sombre group that made its way into the woods at dusk – more than thirty women and children in the Dugas and Bois families, including the four de la Tour girls. They made their way in silence, as if even the children understood that they had entered into a different world and a new way of being. The family of Amalie Boudreau, one of Anne's oldest friends, was to join them, but at the very last minute Amalie decided that she could not bear to abandon her frail elderly father to die alone at the poste, nor could she let her children go into hiding without her. She and Anne embraced silently, and Amalie led her children back to the fort.

Anne knew they could not go far that evening, but the important thing was to get away from La Petite Rochelle. Having spent almost five years along the North Shore, she knew something about the terrain. There was a Mi'kmaw trail that would take them near Nipisiguit, if they could find the head of it. And there were areas where they might find some kind of shelter in abandoned campsites. They had brought with them the pitifully meagre provisions they had on hand, but it was summer so there would be berries and roots to eat and clear spring water to drink.

Anne knew the strength of her children and of Marguerite and her brood, but she was unsure of Jeanne. She was not unsympathetic toward her sister-in-law, but she had to be realistic. Anne knew that her own mother would have said, "It is in the hands of le bon Dieu." *Well, Maman*, she thought, *heaven forbid*.

In spite of everything she had been through so far in her life, Jeanne had never had to sleep in the open. She was determined to be as strong as the others and to help as much as possible, but she soon realized that she was more of a hindrance than a help, so she took charge of her own brood and followed the others. She marvelled at how Anne managed and led the group and at how little guidance the children needed.

When they stopped at dusk to camp beside streams, the older children cut branches from pine or spruce trees to make paillasses to sleep on. When they came across berries or edible roots they picked them. The older boys managed to catch some trout in the streams. Anne doled out the rations, bit by bit. The children received more than the adults and Jeanne was not sure that Anne herself ate anything at all.

Anne was worried because she was having difficulty finding the trail that would lead them in the direction of Nipisiguit. Jeanne wondered if they could find their way there without the trail, but said nothing. On their third day walking they came upon it by chance. It was much easier to follow the trail than to walk in the bush and they made better time. That evening they came across an abandoned campsite and slept under rough shelter. The children went scrounging in abandoned kitchen gardens and returned with a few shrivelled vegetables.

The remaining few days were much the same. As they started out on their last day, they met a Mi'kmaw man. He was not from the settlement near La Petite Rochelle, but he greeted them as friends. He did not have any news of the battle in the Baie des Chaleurs, but he told them they were very close to the area of Nipisiguit.

Jeanne asked him if he should see Jean Sauvage or his nephew Martin would he please tell them that he had seen the Dugas and Bois families here.

They arrived at Nipisiguit in the afternoon and were greeted by other Acadians from La Petite Rochelle. There was some semblance of order amid the chaos. Jeanne was amazed at the strength and competence of these Acadian wives and mothers and at how Anne and Marguerite simply became part of their group of leaders.

They had arranged for the various families to camp in different areas. They were using three abandoned campsites nearby and had built rough shelters from branches for several others. They had pooled their food rations and arranged for groups to pick berries and roots and for others to fish. One group had scrounged everything edible from the abandoned campsite gardens. They were managing to cook on a hearth in a partly destroyed house. The campsites were full, but Anne said that rough shelters would be welcome and some of them would sleep in the open.

Marie-Cécile Landry, a small, leathery-skinned woman who seemed to be the head of the refugee mothers, asked them for what rations they had, if any. They had almost nothing left, but Anne handed the food over to her. Marie-Cécile then gave them a meal which in normal times they would have found insufficient, but here was more than they would have managed on their own.

Lethargy seemed to settle over them after they had eaten, perhaps because of their great weariness, perhaps because of the lessening of tension now that they had found refuge. Anne said they should go to their camp and put the children to bed. Marie-Cécile asked the women to come back to see her later.

Jeanne had felt more like one of the children throughout all of this. Even though she had lived at La Petite Rochelle for a year, she knew she had not experienced what these women had – what had made them so strong. After the children were bedded down, Anne suggested that Jeanne stay to keep on eye on them. Jeanne refused. She knew the older children were quite capable of keeping an eye on the others, and she followed Anne and Marguerite back to the main camp.

Marie-Cécile offered them some herbal tea she had brewed. "Ah," Marguerite remarked, "this is what my mother used to do when she had to give someone bad news." Marie-Cécile flinched and they all stared at her.

She did not speak right away. She quietly sipped her tea and the three other women did the same. Finally, she spoke.

"We had a visit from a Mi'kmaw warrior yesterday," she said in a quiet voice. "He told us that the British have defeated the French at the Baie des Chaleurs. The three French ships are lost. I am sure that is not a surprise to you. But the British have also ravaged and burnt down La Petite Rochelle. They killed all the Acadians, the French and the Mi'kmaq they could find. They did not take prisoners."

The three Dugas women sat silent and still, focused on Marie-Cécile's words.

"The warrior said that some militia and resistance leaders escaped. They were able to go up the rivière Ristigouche in small boats, where the large British warships couldn't follow. We asked about all the people we could think of, but he did not have many names. I know that my husband and my..." she gave a sob, "my one remaining son were killed. The Mi'kmaw was not sure, but thought that the Dugas brothers might have escaped.

"I also asked about Marie Braud," she continued after a slight pause. "I knew her. He said that she and her husband

Michel Benoist were slain and scalped. I didn't mention that, did I? They scalped their victims."

Jeanne felt as if she had turned to stone. When Anne and Marguerite stood up to leave, still without uttering a word, she silently followed them as if in a trance.

Jeanne went to her paillasse in one of the shelters and lay down with Marie, Pierrot, Angélique and Nono, but throughout the long night she did not sleep. As the first rays of dawn appeared, she kissed her sleeping children. Then, without being aware of doing so, she grabbed her bundle of treasures and walked into the forest, putting one foot ahead of the other. She did not think. She did not feel. She would stop breathing if she could.

Chapter 33

Martin Sauvage found Jeanne at dusk, several leagues from where she had left her group to go deep into the forest. She was standing near a brook and looking up at an almost full moon that was just becoming visible over the tree line. Martin quietly walked up behind her and gently put a hand on her shoulder. "Jeanne," he whispered softly.

She whirled around in the semi-light to see a Mi'kmaw warrior in war paint, armed with a musket and a hatchet. A look of sheer terror appeared on her face.

"Jeanne, it's Martin. I'm sorry if I frightened you," he said in a soothing voice.

She gasped. She tried to speak but could not utter a word. She flapped a hand as if to dispel an apparition.

"Jeanne, come with me."

She shook her head. She took a few steps away from the brook and tried to run, but tripped over some roots. She lay on the ground, her body curled and her face turned away from him in stony silence.

He knelt beside her. "Jeanne, everyone is worried and afraid for you. Come with me." She did not move.

Martin quickly cut some pine branches and laid them on the ground and spread his blanket-robe on top of them. He went to the stream and washed the war paint off his face, then carried Jeanne over to the paillasse of branches and laid her down on it. "Can you speak to me, Jeanne?" he asked.

She tried, but could not utter any words. She was shivering. He knew she was in shock. He lay down and wrapped his arms around her to stop her trembling. She clung to him. Martin held her to him silently for some time, and then started whispering to her.

"Jeanne, you've had a bad shock. Anne told me. How they died. How it happened. And this came on top of a lot of other bad things, didn't it? My poor Jeanne. My poor sweet Jeanne." She still could not speak. Then her body shook with a spasm and the tears came. She sobbed uncontrollably, Martin holding her tightly to absorb her sobs.

He crooned softly to her in his own language as he had done with Nono when bringing him to Jeanne.

Finally, her tears subsided and her voice returned. "I'm sorry, Martin," she gasped.

"No, don't be sorry. Can you talk to me now?" She choked back a sob.

"It's because Marie and Michel were killed and then ... mon Dieu! ... then they scalped them!" She was speaking in a hoarse, low voice, as if she was afraid the forest or maybe God might hear her.

"Marie never had a life of her own. And finally she met Michel and she was so happy ... Michel loved her, he really loved her." Jeanne babbled on between sobs. "I wanted to stay with her at the poste and Anne wouldn't let me.... And they were scalped! Marie, who never hurt anyone in her life! She was scalped! If we didn't live in this terrible world it would not have happened...." She gasped for breath.

"It is a terrible thing to scalp someone, Jeanne." Martin hesitated. "But my people do it, the French, the Acadians and the English do it too."

"But why Marie, who was so good and so innocent? Why should she be destroyed at her moment of happiness?" She sobbed again and shook her head. She felt an overpowering anger. After a long pause, she drew a ragged breath.

"Tell me, Martin," she said in a calmer but still angry voice, "if our children and grandchildren survive and tell our stories, will the women and children be remembered? Or will they only talk about the kings, the governors, the militiamen and the warriors? Will anyone remember that innocent women and children were scalped too? Tell me. Tell me, Martin," she demanded angrily.

He was glad to see her angry. It would serve her better than despair.

"I don't know, Jeanne. But I do know that those who survive must go on. You are grieving for Marie Braud and Michel and that is proper. Now you must think of Marie and Pierrot and Angélique and the little orphan. Pierre. All your family."

Her eyes filled with tears again. "No, I don't think it matters. They don't need me."

"Don't say that. It's not true."

"It is true. Anne is the strong woman in the family. She has been wonderful to all of us. My children and Nono adore her. Did you know that Pierrot has named your orphan 'Nono'? Anne would be very good to them. She has been a wonderful mother to the de la Tour girls and the twins. I could not have found my way here as she did. I'm useless."

"Jeanne, you have been through many bad things and your spirit is very sad. Ask your god to help you."

"No, Martin. Go away. Leave me." The tears started again, as she pushed him away and got up from the paillasse. He grabbed her arm.

"Jeanne, you can't walk away in the dead of night. Stay with me and talk to me. We don't have to talk about God."

"No? Well why not? Where is le bon Dieu when we need Him? Why did He let us Acadians build a nation and then let it be taken away from us? Why can't He arrange for us to have just a small corner of this very big land to live on peacefully? Why did He send us missionaries who only care about France, not about Acadia? Why did these missionaries talk to us only about a reward after we die? Why don't they want us to find at least a little contentment on this earth? And why, why, why have the Mi'kmaq accepted to be ruled by such a God?"

She stopped – horrified at having let herself be carried away by her anger. "I'm sorry, Martin. I'm so sorry," she gulped. She looked into the darkening forest again, as though someone or something might have heard her.

"Jeanne, let me tell you the story of how my people accepted your god, as I have heard it from our elders." Jeanne hesitated, then lay wearily in his gentle arms.

"Many moons ago," he began, "soon after your people came here, our Grand Chief Membertou entered into a concordat with your god and the French. The concordat recognized us as a Christian nation and this meant that we could sell our furs to the French. But we did not sell our spirit to your god.

"We have tried to keep the best of our traditions and those of your religion. For example, Sainte-Anne is our patron; as the grandmother of Jesus, she is an elder and this is important to us.

"Our faith in the Great Spirit is deeply connected with the land. We believe that all living things – plants, animals, people and Mother Earth herself – have God within them and must be respected."

Martin paused briefly, and then said quietly, "We must not lose our land."

"What are you thinking about, Jeanne?" he asked.

"Saint-Anne. The beautiful statuette you gave me. She is one of my treasures."

"Then pray to her, Jeanne, when your spirit is weak or sick."

"Yes...." Then she exclaimed, "My bundle! I brought my bundle of special things with me and now I have lost it. Mon Dieu, I did it without thinking. I am so selfish. I left my children behind, but I brought my bundle with me...."

"Your spirit was sick. It's not your fault."

Her eyes filled with tears again. "I think ... I think maybe these things in my bundle remind me of who I am." She sniffled. "Well, I guess I am no one now." She tried to laugh, but gave a strangled sob instead.

"Jeanne, I found your bundle. That's how I found you."

"You have it, Martin?"

"Yes." He reached into the darkness at the edge of the paillasse and gave her the bundle.

She sat on her heels, with the bundle on her knees, and covered her face with her hands for a few moments. Then, almost as if to prove to him how childish she was, she showed him the things inside it. The shawl, her portrait, the books and the statuette of Sainte-Anne.

"Jeanne, would you give me something?"

She hesitated then shyly offered him the small portrait of her young self in the blue silk gown.

"Thank you." He smiled. "We will go back in the morning. Now you must sleep."

He started to say something else, but she put her hand gently on his lips. "Shush." Then she lay down in his embrace.

—

It was only when they were walking back to camp the follow-ing morning that Jeanne thought to ask Martin why he had been the one to look for her.

"A Mikmaw friend saw you two days ago. He told me where you were. When I arrived at the camp yesterday, Anne told me you were missing. She was very worried and didn't know what to do. She did not want to upset your children, but your little Marie knew your special bundle was gone and she too was worried."

"Ah, mon Dieu...."

"Jeanne, you are here, you are going back to your chil-dren. That is the important thing. I am very happy that I found you. I was coming here to tell you and the others that the Dugas brothers and your husband were not captured in the battle. I have not seen them myself but it was reported. I'm not sure where they are now, but Anne expects them to make their way here when they can."

"Dieu merci! I—"

"Jeanne, please don't say you're sorry."

—

They arrived at the camp at midday. As they came out of the woods, Jeanne could see a group of people watching for her. She waved and ran towards her children. They all threw them-selves at her, except for Marie.

"Maman, where did you go?" asked Pierrot. Nono par-roted, "Maman, where did you go?" Angélique clung to her. Marie watched her quietly.

"Well, Maman went into the woods to pick some berries, and she got lost. Luckily, Uncle Martin came along and found me. I didn't find any berries," she said as she tried to smile.

"Well, Jeanne," said Anne, "you are back safe and sound that that is all that matters. Come, you must be hungry."

Marie went to Martin. "Uncle Martin, is Maman all right?"

"Yes, of course, she is. But sometimes Maman needs help too, so now you're getting big enough to help her aren't you, Marie?"

"Yes. Thank you for finding her for us."

Anne asked Martin to eat with them but he said he had to go. "I will pass the word along that the Dugas and Bois families are here," he said, "and the others who have given me their names."

Jeanne watched him slip quietly away, then turned to Anne. Her sister-in-law put a strong arm around her and said, "Come, Jeanne, we don't need to talk about this, now or ever, if you don't want to. We have all been through terrible events, but we have to keep going, no matter what happens. The women who give in to total despair are the ones who have no one who needs them. Your children need you. We all of us need you."

"But Anne," Jeanne insisted, "it's so dreadful ... have you thought of your friend Amalie ... what about her?"

An expression of pain and sorrow surfaced on Anne's face, but was quickly erased. "I know, Jeanne," she said. "But I can't let myself dwell on it, not now. I have to keep moving. We all have to. Perhaps we will find time to grieve in the future. Not now."

Abashed, but grateful that her actions were not to be questioned, Jeanne walked away with Anne, her children hanging on to her skirt.

Chapter 34

It was almost the end of August before the men arrived. They made up a defiant if small Acadian refugee armada. The *Marie-Josèphe*, the *Saint-Charles* and the *Angélique* were among them. Ti-Jos spotted them when they were just specks on the horizon. He waited until he was sure they were not British warships before he ran to tell the others. "I know, I just know one of them is Papa's ship, the *Marie-Josèphe*," he told his Aunt Jeanne.

There was a flurry of tense excitement at the news. The women and children gathered quietly, in small groups, speaking in whispers as if they might be heard from out at sea. They did not dare go directly to the landing spot a short distance away or show themselves on the shore in case Ti-Jos was wrong. There were surely British warships around and privateers and ordinary thieves. Besides, Anne had told them she thought the men would have lost their ships and would arrive overland.

Jeanne thought her heart would break if the ships suddenly changed direction and sailed by. But no, they were headed directly for the landing near them. Suddenly, Ti-Jos gave a cry and started to run. "It's them. It's them."

Jeanne shouted to Ti-Jos to wait, but he was already half-way to the landing, with Pierrot and Nono and the other children and the mothers following.

It took some time for the men to disembark because there was only space for one ship at a time at the little landing space. The *Marie-Josèphe* was the first ship to reach land. Joseph almost stepped on Ti-Jos, who was dancing around him in excitement. He gave his son a rough hug. "Ti-Jos, my man, can you go and keep a lookout for ships, the way I taught you?"

Ti-Jos was off like a bolt of lightning for his lookout spot.

Jeanne could see that Joseph was tense. He looked at the assembled families.

"Mesdames, I know you are very anxious to know who is with us, but I must ask you to be patient. We have supplies and we have to unload them as quickly as possible and then find a place to hide our ships." Some men were beginning to unload the *Marie-Josèphe* as he spoke. He noticed two young boys struggling to pull a small canoe to the shore to help. "Oui, les gars," Joseph said and told one of his men to help the boys. "We can use that boat."

As soon as his ship was unloaded, Joseph sailed it away and the next ship came in. In the meantime, the canoes went back and forth. As each ship was unloaded it followed Joseph's ship up the rivière Nipisiguit to find a secluded corner in which to hide.

Anne and Marie-Cécile Landry took charge on shore. They decided what the women and older children could carry and had them take as much as possible to the nearest campsite.

Finally, the ships were empty and secured on the river. The men were back and had carried the heavier provisions up to the camp. Everyone had worked quickly, efficiently and almost silently.

It was a bittersweet reunion. Abraham's ship had been lost and his wife Marguerite was despondent that it was not among the others when they returned. Fortunately he had only lost his ship and returned with his brother Charles. A number of the returning men had lost their ships too. Marie-Cécile Landry, who had heard that her husband and son were lost, wept with joy when her son found her. Many others' hopes were dashed. Young Anne-Marie Gautier, expecting her first child in a few months, was informed by her brother-in-law that her husband had died in battle. Almost all of the men who arrived found family, but not all the waiting families found their men. Among the men who arrived were some of the most experienced resistance leaders, such as Joseph Leblanc dit Le Maigre, the brothers Pierre and Jean Gautier, Paul Landry, Joseph Richard and Abraham Boudreau.

Pierre Bois had been wounded. He limped off the *Angélique* and tried to run to his family. "Stay, Pierre," Jeanne called, "we're coming!" He scooped up the children in his arms and Jeanne wrapped her arms around him. He wanted to help unload his ship, but Jeanne stopped him. She would take good care of him.

Finally, a hush descended on all of them. Joseph asked his brother Charles to speak.

Charles laughed. "My brother is a man of action. I only get to speak when things are quiet. You women have done un beau travail here. Wherever you are, you women of Acadia, we men know it's our home and our land.

"We have brought all the supplies we could get our hands on," he continued. "We even have a couple of kegs of rum and I hope you will forgive us if we have un p'tit coup to celebrate our reunion. Tomorrow we will speak of more serious things."

—

In the following days, the men took stock of the location and condition of the encampments and the women took stock of the new supplies.

When the men agreed that their situation was good, they quickly began to repair what houses could be salvaged and to build others. They cut down suitably sized pine trees, squared them, put them one upon the other, and fastened them with wooden pegs. They filled the crevices with moss and secured the chimneys with clay. This made a snug house that could withstand the harsh winters.

The women dealt with the barrels of flour, dried cod and the salt that would allow them to cure fish. There were blankets, shoes and clothing. But the provisions had to be carefully doled out. The most valuable of all was the flour. They would stretch it out by baking bread only at intervals of one or two weeks. The winter would be long, and they could not depend on further privateering for supplies.

—

Pierre Bois found himself, perhaps for the first time in his life, the centre of his wife's attention. He had been shot in the leg during the battle at Ristigouche. The wound had not been properly treated and had festered. Jeanne insisted that he stay off his feet and she put a poultice of herbs on his wound. Marie was her mother's assistant, and Pierrot and Nono ran circles around their Papa while he held Angélique on his lap.

"Well, Jeanne," he said one day with typical Acadian wit, "if I had known I would be so well treated, I'd have shot myself in the leg long ago."

Jeanne did not answer. She could not quite explain to herself why she suddenly felt such a surge of affection for her husband.

Pierre recovered in time to help build their own winter house. As the workload lessened, Jeanne once again was privy to her brothers' discussions. Charles had almost convinced Joseph that if they could stay hidden for now and not do anything to further incite British anger, they might have a chance to settle in this area. It was good country. They could live by fishing and hunting, and the land could be farmed if only they could stay long enough in one place. There were other Acadians in the Nipisiguit area, and in Caraquet, Ristigouche and Chipagan. And there had been Mi'kmaw communities here for centuries.

"Think about it, Joseph," Charles said. "Let the rest of the world go by. We can make our home here without anyone being the wiser."

"Charles, you're too good a man to see evil in anyone," said Joseph. "Do you think the British will just forget about us Acadians?"

"They might if we leave them alone. We don't need to raid their ships if we can live off the land. Can't we at least try this?"

"What about the other resistance leaders?"

"What about them? They are at the end of their resources too."

"Well, Charles, let's get through the winter and then see what spring brings."

Mon Dieu, thought Jeanne, *we are back to waiting through another winter to learn what news spring will bring.*

Late in September, they heard that Montréal had fallen. On September 8, a year after the French troops had been defeated on the Plains of Abraham and surrendered Québec, Montréal had surrendered without a shot being fired. Québec, Montréal, La Petite Rochelle were no more. The Acadian refugees were now truly abandoned on this vast continent.

—

The weather was kind to them until late October, when a fierce storm of wind and rain hit the area as if it would never end. At one point, everything in and out of the houses was soaked and they could not even start a fire. One day Joseph was at Jeanne's house and he and Pierre were trying to find something that would be dry enough to respond to the flint. Jeanne handed them her stack of bibliothèque bleu volumes. "Here," she said and walked away. Once a fire had taken hold, Joseph and Pierre took glowing embers to the neighbouring houses.

Jeanne knew very well that to the people around her, a few books meant nothing compared to having a fire. But she could not help but feel a great sadness. *Martin*, she *thought, my spirit is sick. Bonne Sainte-Anne*, she prayed silently, *please help us*.

A few days later, she was called to the bedside of young Anne-Marie Gautier. It was the young woman's first baby and she was terrified. Jeanne smiled. "I have brought many babies into the world. You'll be fine. And I have Sainte-Anne with me. She is the patron saint of mothers in labour, and she will protect you. You'll see." Anne-Marie's labour was long, but she bravely gave birth to a healthy baby boy. Jeanne baptized him.

As Jeanne was leaving, Anne-Marie's brother-in-law arrived with his mother and they began to fuss over the new mother and baby. Jeanne thought that the young man looked rather like a happy father. *Merci, bonne Sainte-Anne.*

—

Through the early autumn, the men heard rumours that the British were destroying Louisbourg. At first the stories were ignored; such a thing was hard to believe. Why would they destroy that strong fortress and important commercial centre for which they had fought so hard?

Charles thought differently. "No," he said, "I can understand. Now that they have taken all the French territory, and they have their own fort at Halifax, they don't need Louisbourg anymore."

"But why destroy it?" asked Jeanne.

"Hmpf, to make sure the French can never have it again," said Joseph. Charles reluctantly nodded.

In mid-November, Joseph Leblanc dit Le Maigre, the Gautier brothers and several Mi'kmaq returned from a scouting mission to Cap Breton and reported that Louisbourg was now totally demolished. Three British ships had arrived in the spring, carrying a company of miners, for the purpose of blowing up the fortress. They dug galleries between the walls, filled them with explosive powder and laid fuses. For many weeks the harbour of Louisbourg echoed with blasts that sent the stoneworks of the fortress skyward. Some of the more valuable ones had been salvaged and shipped elsewhere. The once-mighty fortress at Louisbourg now existed only in its ruins and in the memories of those who had lived there.

A group of the refugees had gathered to greet the Gautiers and the Mi'kmaq and to hear their news, but it did not incite a loud and vigorous discussion the way it might under different circumstances. The mood was silent and anguished.

Charles noticed that René Thérriaux had his violin with him and he asked him and Pierre Gautier if they would play and sing.

They began with "C'était toi, noble empereur qui m'avais mis gouverneur de Louisbourg," which described the defeat of the fortress. As Thérriaux's violin kept a mournful accompaniment they sang "La Prise de Louisbourg." But when Pierre Gautier started to sing "Cruelle partance," describing happy days at the fortress and the pain of leaving friends, Jeanne could not bear to listen anymore. She tried to leave quietly, but her husband saw her go and followed.

"Jeanne, you mustn't. I know it's hard for you. Cry if it will help, but don't run away from us. We need you. We can't survive without you. I can't survive without you. Please come inside. You're not dressed for the cold." Coming from her husband, these few words of encouragement and love constituted a speech, and Jeanne was touched.

She turned and let him put his arm around her and lead her back to the house. "I'm all right, Pierre," she said with a heavy heart. As they walked into the house, she saw Anne watching her, and she nodded to her: *I'm all right.*

—

Once again the winter season brought a breathing space to the families. It was almost comforting to Jeanne to hear the familiar discussions and arguments that took place between the three Dugas brothers, her husband Pierre, Joseph Leblanc dit Le Maigre and some of the other resistance leaders.

There was a new political aspect to be considered. Was the territory of the Baie des Chaleurs and the surrounding area now under the jurisdiction of Halifax or of Québec? If Québec, this would mean some protection under the terms of the general surrender of Nouvelle France signed in Montréal in the fall. If they were still under the jurisdiction of Halifax, they had no assurance whatsoever of their fate. In reality, they did not even know if this distinction in territory had been made.

The Acadians in this area were, for all intents and purposes, in a sort of no-man's land. As always, they would have to wait to see what the spring brought.

Part 4
Capture and
Imprisonment

Chapter 35

The spring of 1761 arrived quietly in Nipisiguit with gentle weather, almost as if it sensed that it must not draw attention to itself or its refugees. Charles and Anne took their family back to their house in Caraquet. Abraham and Marguerite stayed on to help Joseph's family, who were to share their schooner with Abraham. There was an attempt among the women to think in terms of a normal life, and Jeanne and the others scrounged whatever seeds and cuttings they could to start their kitchen gardens. There was no evidence of new supplies, though Jeanne was not aware of any privateering activity. The winter had been difficult, but no one had died of starvation. They had all survived, or rather endured.

—

Alexander Murray, the British governor of Québec, was angry because some of the Acadian privateers along the North Shore had continued their activities even after their defeat at the Ristigouche Poste and the destruction of La Petite Rochelle. He was determined that an end should be put to these raids. In April, he wrote to Colonel Amherst: "Now is the time to evacuate that country entirely of the neutral French and to make the Indians of it our own."

In early July he authorized Pierre du Calvet, the former storekeeper at Ristigouche Poste, to take a census of all the Acadian refugees remaining on the North Shore and to determine the number of extra ships needed to transport them to Québec.

Du Calvet arrived in the area on the sloop *Sainte-Anne* later in July, bearing his instructions. Despite his earlier betrayal, the refugees welcomed du Calvet among them. The idea of a census was not so threatening. At least it recognized their existence and appeared to place them under Québec's jurisdiction.

There was, of course, much discussion and arguing. Not everyone trusted du Calvet, especially Joseph Dugas, but what choice did they have? Very few of the refugees wanted to go to Québec, and they had learned from experience that if they could stall long enough they might be left in place. The former storekeeper spent more than two months travelling from one settlement to the other and left with a very thorough list of the refugees, their locations and their ships.

There was an easing of tensions after du Calvet's departure. They were living as if they were no longer under siege. People walked boldly along the shore, their ships sailed freely between their settlements, and Acadian voices were raised loud again, whether in argument or laughter or song. The children, taking their cue from their elders, ran about and played with abandon. The only real worry Jeanne had concerned her brother Charles. After a recent visit to him in Caraquet, Joseph reported that Charles was sick. She thought of asking Pierre to take her to see him, but she knew that Anne was more than capable of looking after him.

The autumn weather was kind to them again and gave its own beauty to the area. Jeanne was not sure which she preferred, the vibrant autumn colours or the sweet green of spring. Both filled her with a simple joy. She counted her blessings. They had a home and were looking forward to an easier winter than the last, thanks to their hard work during the summer.

—

In November, disaster struck.

Three British warships arrived led by Captain Roderick MacKenzie and a company of about fifty Highlanders. They were guided by Étienne Echbock, chief of the Mi'kmaq at Pokemouche, one of the districts that had made a peace agreement with the British. Pierre du Calvet's census had been ordered by the Governor of Québec, but MacKenzie's orders came from Colonel Forster, commander of the British troops in Nova Scotia. MacKenzie had orders to capture all the Acadians in the Baie des Chaleurs and Miramichi areas.

Captain MacKenzie arrived first at Nipisiguit, rousing Jeanne from her reverie on the beauty of the land. She had turned to look to the sea and was shocked to see a band of men in British military dress marching up from the beach with muskets at the ready. They came right to her. Her neighbours stood watching, some of the hardier among them coming to stand with her. The militia had now started to move to surround them, and a French-speaking militiaman addressed them.

"Mesdames, Messieurs. I speak on behalf of Captain Roderick MacKenzie. You are hereby ordered, by the commander of the troops of the British king in Nova Scotia, to come with us. You may bring a small bundle of personal effects with you."

"But Monsieur," said René Gaudet, one of the few men present, "you must explain to us why this is happening. We have given a census to the governor of Québec and therefore we come under Québec's jurisdiction. Not Nova Scotia's."

The young militiaman snorted. "Well, it does not much matter, does it? Come on, move. If you resist we will have to kill you. And don't think you can escape into the woods."

How could such a dreadful thing happen on such a beautiful day? Jeanne ran to gather her children and to warn the others, while she tried to think calmly. She told the other women that she thought it was all a mistake and that when their husbands could speak to these men and explain about the census they would be released. She quickly made several bundles, each with a change of clothes, extra moccasins, bits of food, a blanket. To her own bundle, she added the statuette of Sainte-Anne and the shawl.

"Tell me what to do, Maman," begged Marie. "I can help."

"Keep an eye on your two brothers and your sister, Marie, promise me?"

"Yes, Maman."

Small groups of women and children started to gather on the beach. Jeanne kept an eye out for Marguerite and her children and Joseph's children.

MacKenzie and his militiaman came back to Jeanne.

"Where are the ships, Madame?"

"The men have taken them out."

"All of them?"

"I'm not sure, Monsieur."

"Where do they keep them?"

"Here, or up the rivière Nipisiguit."

Jeanne was aware that René Gaudet was trying to catch her eye, but she avoided looking at him. Please don't make things worse, she tried to silently warn him.

MacKenzie turned to his aide. "We'll have to put these people in the hold of our ship," he said reluctantly. "Go to it."

"The men have found two families. One has a very sick elderly man and the other a woman about to give birth. What do we do with them?"

"Damnation! Leave them. And one of the women to look after them, but not someone capable of running to give the alarm."

"Sir!"

"Do you women know where your men are? We know a number of Acadian resisters who have been harassing British ships are based here. Where are these men?"

Jeanne replied, "They could be anywhere, Monsieur, we have no way of knowing." This was, after all the truth.

The refugee women and children were roughly pushed down to the shore, taken out by shallop to the British ships, and packed into dark, dirty, smelly holds.

Chapter 36

Captain Roderick MacKenzie and his Highlanders proceeded to capture Acadian refugees at Caraquet, Chipagan, Ristigouche, and all the other places listed in du Calvet's census. A few places managed to hear the news before their arrival and families were able to flee into the forest. When MacKenzie arrived at Néguac, they found the village abandoned. In all, they captured almost eight hundred prisoners – men, women and children – and thirteen ships.

In the end, MacKenzie could not take all the captured Acadians with him, but he made sure that he had the key troublemakers, men like Joseph Leblanc dit Le Maigre and his son Paul, whose ships were armed and equipped for privateering. Charles Dugas, because he was ill, was not taken prisoner. He remained in Caraquet with Anne and their children.

MacKenzie left with more than three hundred men, women and children packed into three warships and about half of the captured Acadian ships. The Acadian men who were allowed to sail their own ships with one or two Highlanders on board knew that their families were being held hostage in the holds of the British ships. The unused Acadian ships were destroyed or burned, as were the houses and equipment. Supplies were confiscated. Stocks of dried fish and even household furniture and other items were taken. Acadian refugees left behind would have no means to travel and would face a very difficult fight for survival in the coming winter.

Chapter 37

In the hold of the ship carrying Jeanne and Marguerite, the prisoners fell silent when they sensed they were headed out to sea. Even the children stopped asking questions their mothers could not answer. Their captors had not told them where they were going or what would happen to them. Were they being taken somewhere in Nova Scotia? Were they being deported? Had their husbands been captured too? After a few hours at sea, a crewman brought them some water to drink, but no food. They plied him with questions, but he said not a word.

The hopes that Jeanne had pinned on the census and Québec quickly disappeared. There was no evidence that an error had been made. What would happen to them now? Would they be reunited with their husbands? Jeanne and Marguerite did not need to remind each other of the stories of families torn apart during the deportations in 1755 and 1758. Jeanne could feel the outline of Sainte-Anne in her bundle and she kept one hand on the statuette in a desperate plea for her help.

It was getting dark when they made land, they knew not where. Hungry, tired and apprehensive, they were grateful to at least be out of the hold of the ship and able to breathe clean air again. Some of the children had slept, but now they were fussing and upset.

Men were waiting for them with torches to light their way. René Gaudet asked one of them where they were.

"Fort Cumberland," was the curt answer.

"Have any other prisoners been taken here from the Baie des Chaleurs?"

"Some. Come on now, move!"

René Gaudet walked beside Jeanne. "This is Beauséjour," he said. Seeing Jeanne's pale, stricken face, he added, "I'm sure they must have brought the others here."

They were quickly shuffled into casements and underground storage rooms with dirt floors. Clearly, these buildings were not meant to be used as a prison. As they entered they were handed a piece of black bread for each family member and one jug of water for the family group. There was no way to tell if any other families or husbands had arrived before them.

Early the following morning they were taken outside into an open area to join the other refugees taken prisoner at the Baie des Chaleurs and the Miramichi. Captain MacKenzie was there and the group was under heavy guard. There were tears of joy and relief when families were reunited.

Pierre had all four children clinging to him, and Nono tried to give him the bit of bread he had left. "No, Nono, you have to eat it, so you can grow up to be big and strong and help Papa," Pierre told him. The boy needed no further prompting and ate it hungrily.

An aide of Captain MacKenzie's announced that they were to be taken to Halifax to await deportation. They would sail there in British ships in several stages. Their own ships were confiscated. They would be permitted to leave in family groups. He proceeded to read a list of names of men who would be the first to go, including Joseph Dugas, Abraham Dugas, Joseph Leblanc dit Le Maigre and others. "You will leave today."

These men were all well-known resistance leaders and privateers. Pierre Bois's name was not on the list. Jeanne didn't know if this was a good or a bad thing, but it meant that Marguerite, her children and Joseph's children would go with Abraham.

Joseph started to approach Jeanne, but a guard stopped him. "I just want a word with my sister," Joseph said, and at a nod from Captain MacKenzie, he was allowed to go to her.

Joseph's face looked thunderous. He took her arm and drew her a bit away from the others. The children stayed with Pierre.

"What's happening, Joseph?"

"What's happening? We were betrayed again, Jeanne. And again by Pierre du Calvet, a man who was supposed to be on our side." He shuddered with suppressed anger.

"Jeanne, there is not much time and there is something I must tell you."

"Yes?"

"It's about Martin. Your friend Martin." He hesitated.

"You've seen him?" She was trying to think why Joseph found it difficult to give her news of Martin. "Has his group signed a peace treaty with the British?" she asked.

"No. He was still fighting the British." Joseph paused.

"Jeanne," he said slowly, "Martin was killed in a skirmish with them. I'm very sorry to have to tell you about this." He reached into his coat and brought out a slim pouch made of woven grass. "Martin had this on him. I thought you would like to have it back."

Ah, mon Dieu! She stood in front of Joseph, the colour draining from her face. Martin, dead? Her lips trembled but she could not let herself cry.

Joseph pushed the keepsake toward her. "Take this, Jeanne. It's the portrait of you in your blue silk gown." She swayed. He grabbed her arms to steady her.

"Jeanne, Martin was a wonderful man. I loved him like a brother. But now we have to go on without him. Jeanne! Are you listening to me?" He paused. "He had a wife and children. Did you know that?"

She closed her eyes so that Joseph could not see into her soul. In truth, she had not known, but it would not have changed how she felt about Martin. She opened her eyes and looked at Joseph. "I have a family too," she said softly.

"Yes, you do."

Joseph wrapped his arms around her. "I'm so sorry, Jeanne. We'll see you at Halifax. I don't see how we can be deported before the spring. Take care of Pierre. He's a good man too."

She could only nod in reply.

Jeanne, Pierre and their children were in the last group and sailed two days later. They arrived at the prison on Georges Island in Halifax Harbour on a cold and wet fall day to find the prison sheds allocated to the Acadians already filled to overflowing. They spent their first few nights there sleeping in the rough on wet, muddy, cold ground. They were given rations too meagre to satisfy hunger and filthy blankets too threadbare to provide warmth.

Chapter 38

At the time of the first deportations in 1755, the British had set up prison camps across Nova Scotia. The most important were Fort Cumberland, Fort Anne in Annapolis, Fort Edward in Pisiquit, and Georges Island in Halifax Harbour. During and following the deportations many hundreds of Acadian prisoners were held at Georges Island before their eventual deportation.

But Georges Island was not just a military prison. Ordinary criminals were also confined there and these prisoners were frequently housed in the same sheds as the Acadians. It was not unusual for the Acadians to see men flogged with cat-o'-nine-tails and to witness hangings from the yardarm of a British ship. The sheds were crowded, overrun with vermin and diseases spread quickly. The rooms were dark, water dripped down the walls, and the earth floors were cold and damp. The only piece of furniture in each was a wooden bench. When the sheds were overcrowded, some of the Acadian prisoners were forced to live in the open, exposed to the elements and half-starved. Many of the elderly and the young died there under the stars.

Among the prisoners taken to Georges Island in 1760 and 1761 were several hundred Acadian resisters and privateers. Some of them had been captured by British forces, others had been forced to surrender to avoid starvation. As a result the security measures at Georges Island had been increased and the Acadian resistance leaders and their families were kept in a separate area.

Chapter 39

The prison cell Jeanne and Pierre and their children were pushed into inside the sheds was barely more comfortable than being in the open, but at least there was a roof over their heads. It was shelter.

Jeanne was in a state of shock and trying not to let it show. Pierre's face was grey with worry and fatigue. The children were bewildered and afraid, unused to the rough manners of their keepers. They were alarmed when they heard that Joseph and Abraham and their families were being held under tight security in another part of the prison because of their partisan activities. Above all Jeanne felt abandoned, and even more so now, with the news of Martin's death.

She asked herself what Charles's wife would do. She thought she was beginning to understand Anne's refusal to be emotional. *Just keep putting one foot ahead of the other.*

They quickly learned the routine of the sheds. They shared their plight with the other captives, some of whom they knew from the Baie des Chaleurs. But they all seemed to be afflicted with a strange silence. Although willing to give any assistance they could to fellow sufferers, it was as if no one knew what to say, as if no one remembered any words of comfort or hope.

When Jeanne heard that a young mother was expecting to give birth soon, she passed the word along that she was a midwife. Perhaps she would be allowed to help her. When the time came, a guard appeared late in the night to take her to attend the birth. She brought Sainte-Anne with her and let the young woman clutch the statuette during her ordeal. Prisoners nearby had already complained about the young mother's screams and she was bravely trying to be silent in spite of her pain. Jeanne thought her own heart would break. The young mother was emaciated and her baby pitifully tiny. She heard a few days later that the baby had died.

—

That first winter on Georges Island was agonizing. The cold and dampness took its toll on all of them. Jeanne and Pierre ate as little as possible in order to give most of the rations to the children. Jeanne worried about Angélique, the frailest of her children, but she survived the winter. They had no contact with Joseph or Abraham or their families. For Jeanne, there was a feeling of helplessness and despair such as she had never known. Here there were no comforters, only sufferers. Her biggest fear was that she and Pierre and their children would be deported without knowing what would happen to her brothers and their families.

In the spring, some of the less dangerous Acadian men held in the sheds were allowed to do menial work on the prison island, for which they were paid with increased rations or small sums of money. Eventually, some were allowed to work off the island – ironically on farms that had been taken from Acadians and which their new owners were now having trouble maintaining. Some worked in the town of Halifax. Wages were paid and mostly used to buy extra food.

Pierre was allowed to work on a farm, where he earned a small wage, and he would bring back the food he was given for his meal. When the farmer realized what he was doing, he gave him extra food to take to his family. "You see, Jeanne," Pierre said, "there are good people in the world."

Another blessing from Pierre's work was that he was able to get news of the Dugas brothers. One of the other prisoner-workers had contact with the partisans. They were well; the families had survived the winter. Pierre sent a message back to them.

It was difficult, but life continued in the prison sheds. Jeanne assisted at almost a dozen births during her stay there – and many more deaths. The family of Joseph Broussard dit Beausoleil, perhaps the best known and most feared Acadian resistance fighter, was being held with the ordinary prisoners. Broussard's granddaughter Elizabeth Isabelle was born in the camp and his nephew Joseph Grigoire died there, leaving behind a widow and three small children.

There were marriages too. Because there were no Catholic priests available, Protestant clergymen came to the island prison to perform marriages and baptisms. The Acadians considered them "white" rites that they would have "rehabilitated" by a Catholic priest at the first opportunity. Some of these rehabilitations would eventually be carried out in such far away places as Saint-Malo and Louisiana.

—

The Lieutenant-Governor of Nova Scotia, Jonathan Belcher, was determined to deport the remaining Acadians, even if his commander-in-chief General Amherst and the Lords of Trade in London strongly advised him to allow them to stay in the province. In the summer of 1762, Belcher used several minor incidents of rebellion to justify his plan to rid himself of the "Acadian problem" once and for all.

In mid-August, more than twelve hundred Acadian prisoners were placed on five transport ships that set sail for Boston. Jeanne and Pierre and their children were on one of these ships, but more dangerous resistance fighters such as the Dugas brothers were left behind on Georges Island.

It was Jeanne's worst nightmare come true. Deportation! That which they had tried so long to avoid. Where were they going? They had not been told. How would they survive?

She had worried needlessly. The Massachusetts Council absolutely refused to accept any more Acadians, and after spending almost three weeks in Boston harbour, the ships had no alternative but to return to Halifax and Georges Island.

It was a devastating experience for Jeanne, although their rations on ship were better than in prison and they had the benefit of clean fresh air – once out of sight of land, they were permitted on deck for a few hours each day. But to go through the worry and stress of being torn from their land and then to be returned to prison was a crushing blow.

For a brief moment when they stepped back into their cell, Jeanne thought she just could not go on any longer. Then she turned again for comfort to the attitude of her sister-in-law Anne and of Sainte-Anne. No emotion. Strength. Go on.

—

When Pierre returned from working on the farm one October day, he brought back the news that Joseph and Abraham and their families, together with several other partisans, had escaped from Georges Island. His informant said that he didn't know how they had managed it. They must have had outside help.

Jeanne wept softly. She was not surprised that Joseph had managed to escape. But how could he have left her behind? She knew she was being unreasonable, but in her heart she felt betrayed. Even though she could not expect him to keep the promise he had made to her when she was ten years old – that they would always remain together as a family – she was hurt. Still, she did sincerely hope that he would not be caught and brought back to Georges Island. She knew that other escapees had been unmercifully whipped and sometimes hanged.

—

The winter of 1763 was another heartbreaking period for the Acadian prisoners. The guards at the sheds seemed less and less interested in their care, and there were more incidents of prisoners taking advantage of their fellow captives. Jeanne was appalled at how uncaring some of her fellow Acadian prisoners were, but then weren't they all just trying to survive?

She knew there was theft and prostitution, too. One young widowed mother who thought Jeanne was criticizing her turned on her one day and said, "Jeanne, I'm trying to keep my small ones alive. I do it for extra food. Can you understand that?"

"Yes. I do understand," Jeanne replied. "I'm not judging you. I only wish I could help you instead." Jeanne started to give her bits of food when she could, but she knew it was not nearly enough.

Chapter 40

After seven long years, the war between Britain and France ended with the signing of the Treaty of Paris in 1763, but when the news arrived in Nova Scotia with the first ships in the spring, it did not mean immediate change for the remaining Acadian prisoners on Georges Island.

—

Along with the news of the end of the war, spring brought unusually cold and wet weather and a bad fever that swept through the sheds. Jeanne tried to minister to the sick, but she had no access to herbs or plants or healthy food. When she pleaded with the guards, their superior came to talk to her. He came into the sheds holding a handkerchief over his nose.

"Monsieur," she said, "many of the prisoners have the fever. I can help them if I can get some herbs and plants, and perhaps some fresh food? I'm afraid that without remedies many of the children will die."

"I'm sorry, Madame," was the brusque reply, "but they won't be missed. It will mean fewer Acadians for us to deal with, won't it?" He turned on his heel and walked away.

Pierre, who was standing near Jeanne, shouted, "Monsieur!"

The man did not even turn to look at him.

"Jeanne...." Pierre took in the stricken look on her face. "There is nothing you can do. Come." He put his arm around her to lead her back to their cell.

"Please stay in our cell," he said, "or you too will catch the fever. And give it to the children."

"I think I already have it." She put his hand to her hot, feverish forehead.

Pierre took over. He made her stay in their cell and rest and he kept the children away from her as much as he could. He gave her his rations to eat and as much as he dared to take away from the children.

Jeanne was terrified at what was happening but too weak to do anything about it. She did not even have the strength to pray. "What difference would it make?" she asked Pierre.

"I don't know," he said, "but I'm praying as hard as I can. Jeanne, you can't leave us. Fight! You would fight for me and our children. Fight for yourself."

Le bon Dieu works in strange ways she thought later. She recovered but, inevitably, the children caught the fever. Pierrot, Angélique and Nono all died. Marie caught it too but, being older and stronger, she recovered.

The fever was just leaving Jeanne when her children died, and she was still very weak. Pierrot and Nono slipped away on the same day, best friends to the end. Angélique followed them the next day.

Pierre saw Jeanne try to stand up. "No. No, Jeanne, you're not strong enough." He wrapped the three bodies in an old blanket and some cloths, and brought the bundles to Jeanne so she could touch them one last time.

"I'm taking them to see if someone will help me bury them," he said. "Marie, stay with Maman and make sure she doesn't try to move."

"Yes, Papa."

Marie sat on the ground beside her distraught mother. "Maman," she said, "I'm so sorry. Would it have been better if I had died? Instead of Angélique or Pierrot or Nono?"

Ah, mon Dieu, Jeanne whispered to herself. She pulled Marie into her arms and the tears came.

—

The fate of the remaining Acadian prisoners at Georges Island went unresolved for more long months. Montague Wilmot replaced Jonathan Belcher as Lieutenant-Governor, but in spite of official instructions that he was to use all lawful means to persuade the Acadians to remain in Nova Scotia, he had no intention of releasing the prisoners.

When Wilmot was unable to persuade the Lords of Trade to agree to deport the Acadians, he presented the prisoners with a plan that would discourage them from wanting to stay in Nova Scotia. He led them to believe that the only way for them to obtain their freedom would be to accept deportation. In the fall of 1763, more than six hundred Acadians, led by Joseph Broussard dit Beausoleil, left Halifax in two groups headed for the West Indies.

Others, such as resistance leader Pierre II Surette, refused to leave the land of their ancestors. His family and other followers simply stayed on Georges Island until at last Wilmot was forced to release them. Jeanne, Pierre and Marie were among these last prisoners to be freed in the spring of 1764 – after three long, cold, hungry, tragic years.

Chapter 41

The last refugees to leave the Acadian prison sheds on Georges Island in late spring 1764 were a bedraggled and defeated group. Weary, half-starved, in rags, they silently boarded the shallops that came to take them off the island. Even the guards were silent. It was a shameful end for both captives and captors.

The shallops were headed for Chezzetcook, a small community of Acadian and Mi'kmaw families just a few leagues from Halifax. The Acadians there had been permitted to accompany Abbé Maillard to the Halifax area in 1760. They did some fishing and farming, supplying hay as well as lumber to Halifax. They welcomed the group of Acadians. *With pity*, Jeanne thought, *but then, do we not deserve it?*

Jeanne felt dizzy when they arrived. She didn't know if it was from physical weakness or the strangeness of being free again. Both Pierre and Marie looked at her with concern, for she was as pale as death.

"Madame," she heard Pierre say to an older woman who came to them. "My wife has been ill and she is not strong."

The woman clucked and took Jeanne in hand. "Come with me," she said.

They were all in need of nourishment, rest and hope. These things came, but slowly. By the time winter arrived, most of the group had settled into the life of the community. Several had left Chezzetcook to seek refuge elsewhere and some had returned with news.

Jeanne's brother Joseph had been hiding in Chedabouctou, near Canceau, since his escape from Georges Island in 1762. Soon after his arrival there he had married, in a white ceremony, a woman named Louise Arseneau. Two years later they emigrated to the island of Miquelon. Joseph Leblanc dit Le Maigre, who left Georges Island in 1763 with his son Paul, followed Joseph and his family to Miquelon.

—

Jeanne, Pierre and Marie spent almost two years in Chezzetcook. It was good to be in an Acadian community again. As they regained their strength the men worked at whatever needed to be done and shared in the profits of their labour. Eventually Pierre and two other men started to build a small schooner. Jeanne once again assisted at births and used her skills with herbs and plants to help the sick. During the winter months they learned to laugh and sing again. But old thoughts, like old habits, are hard to shed. The families argued over the merits of staying in Chezzetcook or leaving, and where they might live instead.

During the winter of 1766, they learned that the Robin company had established a fishing outport at Neireishak on Île Madame. Pierre believed there was a chance of earning a better living there, and it would put greater distance between them and the British authorities at Halifax. Jeanne simply wished to live as far away as possible from the prison sheds on Georges Island.

They left in the spring on their new schooner, with another couple, Joseph Richard dit Matinal and his wife Marie Marguerite Thibodeau, to settle at Petit-de-Grat on Île Madame. Joseph Richard was a second cousin of Jeanne, on her mother Marguerite Richard's side. He was worried about his two sisters, Rosalie and Anne. He believed they were somewhere in Cap Breton or perhaps at Chedabouctou, and he was anxious to find them.

—

The land at Petit-de-Grat was rocky and barren and not suitable for farming. Fog that came in off the ocean and enveloped the area in the spring seemed to stay forever. But the port had a fine harbour that was open year round and an abundant supply of fish. They found a couple of empty fishing huts that were very primitive, but luxurious compared to the prison sheds still fresh in Jeanne's mind.

Pierre Bois and Joseph Richard had to learn how to fish for cod commercially and managed to get hired on a large fishing boat that operated out of Petit-de-Grat for the Robin company. It was gruelling work. Pierre knew that if he had come here directly from the prison sheds, the work would have killed him. Jeanne realized he was going through a difficult time and she felt somehow closer to him. Perhaps with her brother Joseph now out of her life she felt herself more completely Pierre's wife – and she was pregnant.

In the summer, she gave birth to a son, Régis. She was touched when she saw the happiness on Pierre's face. She realized with a pang that she had been so wrapped up in her own sorrow over the loss of their three children that she had not really acknowledged his grief. They had not been able to talk about Pierrot, Angélique and Nono since their deaths.

One day when Régis was four or five months old and Pierre was playing with him and making him laugh, he turned to her. "Jeanne," he said, "do you remember how much Pierrot and Nono made us laugh?"

"Yes," she said, letting herself remember. And they were able to talk about the two little boys' and their antics. Jeanne cautiously let herself think that perhaps life could be good again.

—

After two seasons in Petit-de-Grat, Pierre decided they should go to Neireishak, where the Robin business was based. The climate and living conditions would be less harsh there and he could get work as a shipbuilder in the winter months. The Acadians did not have the right to buy property, but some simply settled and built on unused land. Jeanne was reminded of her mother's stories of how they had come to Port Toulouse and then moved on to Louisbourg.

Joseph Richard dit Matinal followed them to Neireishak. They found that more and more Acadians were now coming to Île Madame since they had received permission to do so after the end of years of war. They came from the Baie des Chaleurs, from Port Toulouse, from the prisons, from their hideouts in the forest, and from the places to which they had been deported. All had stories of great hardships. Some talked about their experiences at length, as if it helped to do so, while others preferred to suffer in silence.

Pierre Bois and Joseph Richard quickly found land where they could build simple habitations side by side. They decided to fish with their own schooner for the summer and sell their catch to the Robins. If the catch was good, it was more profitable this way. As anticipated, Pierre found work in shipbuilding in the winter months.

There was no chance for Acadians to become traders on Île Madame. Under the anti-Catholic penal laws, the Acadians could not trade, hold public office, vote, teach, attend school or own land. The British had encouraged men such as the brothers John and Charles Robin to immigrate to Nova Scotia from the Jersey Islands. Being Huguenots, they spoke French and were able to do business with the Acadians. They became prominent businessmen and traders in the region, with privileges and rights that the Acadians were denied. The Jersey men could also occupy the important government and military positions, and they exploited the situation for profit.

—

Life for Pierre, Jeanne and their children was easier at Neireishak. Their house was simple but snugly built against the elements, an improvement over the fishing shacks at Petit-de-Grat. The land not only looked gentler but could be tilled for planting. They had a proper kitchen garden and soon acquired a cow and some hens.

Three years after the arrival of Régis, Jeanne gave birth to a daughter, Geneviève. It was a difficult pregnancy – Jeanne was almost forty years old – but she was happy to have another child. Marie was sixteen when the new baby came, and Jeanne marvelled at how kind and caring Marie was toward her younger siblings, after the hardships she herself had suffered as a child.

In 1770, when Marie was barely eighteen, she met Pierre "Raymond" Poirier. He was almost ten years older than Marie and they knew very little about him or his family – except that he was Acadian. Jeanne was worried. She asked Pierre if they should perhaps at least ask Marie and Raymond to wait until they could have a proper wedding with a priest officiating.

"Jeanne, you know you're just being protective," said Pierre. "Raymond seems to be a decent man and who knows when we'll have a priest attend to us again?"

But life was still so complicated and unsure, Jeanne thought. *What if Marie follows him to God only knows where and she is unhappy? We wouldn't even know.* She confronted her daughter. "Do you love him, Marie?" her mother asked. "This is not just something you think would be convenient? Or the right thing to do? Please tell me honestly," she begged her daughter, remembering her own half-hearted decision to marry Pierre.

"Maman, I'm sure about Raymond and me. Truly. And I won't be leaving you to go somewhere else. Raymond wants to stay here. I do love him, Maman. And I know that I'm capable of loving only one man."

Marie did not mean it unkindly, but Jeanne was a little taken aback. Marie's intelligence and instinct were a constant source of amazement to her mother. Sometimes Marie seemed older than Jeanne herself.

"Very well, Marie," Jeanne said reluctantly and hugged her daughter. "But you do understand that it will have to be a white marriage for now."

"Yes, Maman. Of course, I understand." Marie's face shone with happiness, and she ran off to tell Raymond.

Ah, mon Dieu, Jeanne prayed silently. *If you are not tired of hearing my pleas, keep my daughter safe.*

On a beautiful summer day, Marie and Raymond, as well as another couple, Augustin Deveau and Rosalie Richard, pledged their love before an elder of the Acadian community. Joseph Richard dit Matinal had indeed found his sisters Rosalie and Anne on Île Madame. Anne had married some years before and now had five children; Rosalie had taken refuge with her sister until wedding Augustin Deveau. Traditionally, there was no celebration held for a "white marriage," but seeing the glow of happiness on Marie's face Jeanne realized it was not necessary anyway.

—

The year after Marie's white marriage, the missionary Charles François Bailly came to Île Madame for a pastoral visit and gave his blessing to the white marriages and baptisms that had been held in the absence of a priest. It was a summer full of celebrations.

Two days after the rehabilitation of her marriage, Marie gave birth to a son, Laurent. He was baptized by Abbé Bailly on the same day. Jeanne's children Régis and Geneviève had their baptisms blessed as well. Régis was five years old and Geneviève two.

Abbé Bailly told all the newly blessed participants that they were now living in their "Holy Father's embrace." Not for the first time Jeanne wondered if it made a difference, but she had to admit to herself that it did seem to give their lives structure – even if God often seemed to be indifferent to their needs.

—

The following five years were peaceful. Jeanne's life once again centred on her family. Marie and Raymond lived nearby, as did Joseph Richard dit Matinal. They made improvements to their simple home, enlarged their garden and acquired a few more farm animals.

Jeanne kept a promise she had made to herself. As soon as Régis was old enough, she started to teach him his alphabet and to read and write. She was happy to see that he was a good student. There had been no opportunity to teach Marie when she was young and they were moving from place to place in fear of their lives. Now that Marie was an adult with a family of her own, she was not interested. Jeanne was disappointed, but she understood.

And Jeanne continued her in role as a midwife. She always took the statuette of Sainte-Anne with her and now she also took her embroidered shawl to wrap the babies in when she baptized them. During her stay in the prison sheds, where the poor mothers often had barely a scrap of cloth to dress their babies, wrapping the babies in the shawl while she baptized them seemed to give the ritual some dignity. She wondered still if many of those children survived, though she found that her thoughts returned to Georges Island less and less. The loss of Pierrot, Nono and Angélique, of course, was a wound that would never heal. She included them in her prayers, but was slowly learning to live with it.

Jeanne Dugas was also accepting the loss of her beloved Acadia. Her hope now was to live in peace; that there would be no more wars and that their wandering life was over.

Chapter 42

No one could have foreseen the impact the American Revolutionary War would have on the small enclave of Acadians living on Île Madame. In September 1776, a first-lieutenant with the temporary rank of captain, John Paul Jones, brought his ship, the *Providence*, into the waters off Nova Scotia, looking for supplies and additional crew members. He first raided Canceau, and then went in pursuit of the fishing and transport ships at Neireishak and Petit-de-Grat. With the element of surprise, he was able to capture nine un-armed Jersey ships, as well as others belonging to Acadians and some of their crewmen. He plundered the Robin store-houses, taking a valuable stock of dried cod and a large stock of supplies, and then razed the entire establishment. This was devastating not only for the Robin company but also for the families who depended on it to earn a living.

It was inexplicable. Why would a ship from the British colonies attack Nova Scotia, itself now a British colony? To the Acadians, the behaviour was that of a pirate or a privateer rather than that of a military naval ship and there was no defence against it.

Fearing other assaults, John Robin retreated to Paspébiac on the Gaspé peninsula to join his brother Charles who had established a fishing outport there in the 1760s.

—

On top of all she had been through, coming at a time when she thought they had at last found a peaceful life, this was shattering for Jeanne. It was a repeat of all the fears she had experienced since the first fall of Louisbourg.

Pierre was devastated too. "I'm sorry," he said as if it were his fault.

She just shook her head at him, her eyes filling with tears.

Before leaving, John Robin had encouraged the Acadians on Île Madame to follow him to Paspébiac to continue their fishing activities for his company there. Among a group of Acadians who dutifully followed him there a month or so later were Jeanne and Pierre and their children, and Marie and Raymond Poirier. Joseph Richard dit Matinal, Augustin Deveau and Joseph Gaudet and their families also followed.

—

The barachois of Paspébiac was not even a village – it was simply a fishing outport. Set in an isolated part of the Gaspé peninsula, it was backed by mountains and faced the sea. A triangular sandbar enclosing a lagoon, the barachois was ideal for the shallops used in a shore fishery and it provided an excellent beach for curing fish. Charles Robin had built a successful fishing commerce and there were now substantial buildings and storehouses. However, the housing for the fishermen and their families was no better than on Île Madame.

Two years earlier, John and Charles Robin had encouraged other Acadian exiles in France to return to North America and even carried them across the Atlantic on their ships. Charles brought about eighty of them to settle in Bonaventure and Tracadigache where some had relatives, and John had taken some to Cap Breton. Charles Robin also did business with a Mi'kmaw community at the mouth of the rivière Ristigouche.

The men who came from Île Madame were now old hands at fishing. God knows their wives and children were old hands at picking up stakes and sailing away to seek refuge, thought Jeanne. They felt safe here. She was determined to be strong, but silently prayed they would not remain in Paspébiac for the rest of their lives.

At least she was still useful. Her family needed her. Babies were born. People took sick. Few people came to visit from other communities, but sometimes Mi'kmaq came to visit with their families, causing Jeanne to think of Martin, always with a twinge of guilt. If only she could be sure that his death had not occurred because he was trying to stay in contact with her. Joseph had told her little and she had not dared press him for details. Perhaps she was afraid the answer would only cause her more grief.

They coped. They made their simple fishing shacks more comfortable. Régis and Geneviève grew, and now that Marie was married and making a home of her own, Jeanne was grateful for the two younger children. Before long Marie gave birth to another child, a girl they named Eulalie. Count your blessings, her Maman would have said. And Jeanne did.

—

Then, in June of 1778, barely two years after their arrival at Paspébiac, two heavily armed privateer ships arrived. They seized Charles Robin's ship, the *Hope,* laden with nearly two thousand quintals of dried cod, and sent the ship on to the British colonies. Another ship, also laden with dried cod, was captured a few weeks later. Charles Robin was taken hostage but he managed to escape and fled into the woods at night. He took flight and returned to his home on the island of Jersey. The American privateers continued to ravage the north shore of the Baie des Chaleurs, looting stores at the fishing outports and then burning the empty buildings.

Jeanne and Pierre, their families and others were forced to flee yet again. Somehow, somewhere there had always been a next place for them to go to, but Jeanne had to wonder if God was not being unmercifully stingy with the places He found for them. They were never able to do more than survive at each place and with just enough strength to enable them to move again. Now, they were headed for the Îles de la Madeleine.

"I'm sorry, Jeanne. I'm sure it's only temporary," Pierre said. "The war in the British colonies won't go on forever. And then we'll come back home. I promise."

—

The Îles de la Madeleine are a chain of twelve small islands, most of them connected by sandbars, situated in the golfe du Saint-Laurent, about twenty leagues from Île Royale and twenty-five leagues from Île Saint-Jean.

The Acadians from Paspébiac were sailing for Île Havre-Hébert at the southern tip of the chain, where Richard Gridley, a British colonial army officer and military engineer, had established a fishing outport in 1763, after the end of the Seven Years War. The islands had been used as seasonal fishing outports in previous years, but Gridley had established the first year-round community. He had persuaded, among others, several Acadian families to work for him at Havre-Hébert, fishing for cod and chasing after seals and walrus for their skins and oil during the winter months.

Not all the Acadians from Paspébiac went to the Îles de la Madeleine, but Jeanne and Pierre's group stayed together. Marie and Raymond sailed with her parents and others followed in several shallops.

The living conditions were much the same as at other outports and they were used to living this way. In fact, the weather at Havre-Hébert was more temperate than at Paspébiac, with milder winters and fresh summers. But the wind blew year round – stronger in the winter. When the island was locked in by ice in the winter months, they were truly isolated, with no other land in sight.

The men were used to the cod fishery, but the hunt for walruses and seals out on ice floes in the bitterly cold sea in winter and early spring was numbing. Dressing the walruses and seals was equally hard work. Pierre was the oldest man in the group and Jeanne was afraid it was too much for him, though he would not admit it.

In the spring of 1781, the first ship brought the news that the war between Britain and its North American colonies was coming to an end and that the colonies had won their independence.

Jeanne was determined they should return to Île Madame, or at least to Cap Breton. She shamelessly bullied Marie and Raymond to agree with her. But as the group argued the pros and cons of returning, Pierre was not at all convinced that they should go anywhere. Jeanne wondered if it was because he thought it safer to stay here or because he could not face another move.

Worried and frustrated, Jeanne told him, "I cannot stay silent and just wait to see what you men will decide."

Pierre replied, perhaps only half jokingly, "Well, in any event, you have always had your own way." She looked at him.

"For half our lives," he said, "we followed your brother Joseph." His answer and the truth of it shook her.

"Pierre, I'm sorry. I'm truly sorry. But please, please, listen to me one more time. You did promise me that we would go back." It was decided they would go.

Part 5
The Return Home

Chapter 43

In the early summer of 1781, Jeanne and Pierre, Marie and Raymond Poirier, and their extended families returned to Île Madame. There they found more Acadians than when they had left five years before – people who, like themselves, were eager to live in what had been their homeland. Jeanne and Pierre and their group found that their simple houses had been taken over by these other Acadians. Since they had never had legal ownership of their homes, they could not claim them back. Once more, they started over. Once more, with nothing.

Even their connection with the Robin company was changed. Both John and Charles Robin had retreated to the Jersey Islands during the Revolutionary War. The Robin company was still operating in Neireishak, but much diminished. Other Jerseymen had arrived to do business on the island, such as the Janvrins, Bournots and Malzards. The Robin company no longer had a monopoly, but this did not seem to shift more control to the fishermen.

Joseph Gaudet, Raymond Poirier, and Augustin Deveau took their families to Petit-de-Grat. Pierre Bois and Joseph Richard dit Matinal stayed in Neireishak. Jeanne thanked

God for the decision, for she felt she could not face any more fog-choked months at Petit-de-Grat. But their first fishing season at Neireishak was disappointing and their living conditions very basic.

—

They knew that the Robins had had a seasonal fishing outport on the northern coast of Cap Breton Island since the late 1760s. The area, known as Chétican, was the site of a seasonal Mi'kmaw camp but had no permanent inhabitants. Fishermen of all nationalities had used this convenient spot for their activities for many years before the Robins had arrived. By the late 1770s, the Robin's fishing outport had a large system of wharfs and sheds around the cove known as La Pointe.

After a brief visit there at the end of the 1781 fishing season, Pierre and Joseph Richard contracted to fish for the Robin outport at Chétican the following summer.

The two families spent three summers fishing for the Robin company at La Pointe. They were housed in shacks along the sandbar known as Le Banc opposite the Robin wharf. This was not too uncomfortable during summer months, and the cod catch was very good. At the end of each season, because they were fishing for their own account with their own boats, they came away with a reasonable profit, even after their purchases at the company store were deducted.

Jeanne and Marguerite, Joseph Richard's wife, worked on the flakes on the beach where the cod was dried. During their first summer there, the Robin's manager offered to hire Régis as a full-time worker during the season but Jeanne refused and Pierre agreed with her – Régis was only sixteen years old. In Paspébiac Jeanne had seen boys as young as fourteen recruited, spending their lives working for the Robin company because they were forever in debt to it.

The Robin company at Chétican was obviously doing well, better than that at Neireishak, and there was always a shortage of fishermen and shore workers. The manager asked Pierre and Joseph Richard to consider settling there and to recruit others to come with them. The Robin company, in turn, would make the outport a year-round enterprise. The settlers would have a market for their fish and the company store to provide their needs.

It was a daunting prospect. They would be pioneers – it was absolutely virgin land. The two families discussed it at length during the long summer evenings, and then in the fall with the rest of their Acadian group in Neireishak.

Marie and Raymond were all in favour. Jeanne thought to herself, *They are so young, they don't understand how hard a life it could be*. But conditions in Neireishak and Petit-de-Grat were still difficult and there was for once general agreement that they should not pass up this opportunity. The isolation should mean relative safety from marauding pirates and privateers, they were assured of a market for their fish catches, and the presence of the Mi'kmaq during part of the year would ease their isolation without being a threat. It was agreed that Pierre and Joseph Richard would make final arrangements with the Robin company during the summer of 1784.

They spent the summer of 1785 at Neireishak and Petit-de-Grat, preparing for their move. Early in the fall, Jeanne and Pierre Bois, Marie and Raymond Poirier, Joseph Richard dit Matinal, Augustin Deveau, and Joseph Gaudet and their families sailed for Chétican. Three other Acadian families followed a month later.

Chapter 44

The harbour at Chétican was formed by a peninsula running northward, parallel to the to the mainland. The harbour itself was almost completely closed off by sand deposits, allowing only very shallow small boats to enter. This peninsula, which everyone called "the island," was joined to the mainland by an isthmus – Le Banc. The Robin company had set up its wharf and buildings at the southwest tip of the island to take advantage of the good harbour there.

The coastland was rocky, covered with fir, maple and birch trees, and with mountains in the background. There was a hill facing Chétican Harbour that ran parallel to the peninsula – the island – and a valley was nestled between the hill and the mountains. It would have been logical to make their homes near Le Banc, but the Acadians chose to settle in the valley, hidden from the sea and out of sight of pirates and privateers. The area became known as Le Platin. A smaller group settled to the northeast of Le Platin and this settlement became known as La Petite Étang. Both areas had a good supply of fresh water. They were, however, situated some distance from the Robin company and the harbour where their boats would be anchored.

—

Jeanne and Pierre Bois chose a spot for their new home that was not too heavily wooded and near a sparkling, clear stream. Marie and Raymond picked out a spot nearby but across the stream. Before Jeanne could even voice her thoughts about why the other side, Raymond said, "Belle-Mère, I'm going to build a bridge!" They had to work quickly to build houses before winter set in, but by now they were good at it. Here there was plentiful wood. Their first houses were made log-house style with roughly prepared wood, but they were snug and built to withstand the elements. When the work required more than one or two men, all the others pitched in. As other families arrived, they were ready to help them with their houses.

The Robin company kept their word. The manager and two other staff members stayed over the winter and readily supplied the Acadians with whatever they needed, on credit until the next fishing season.

Pierre and Raymond were full of plans. It did Jeanne's heart good to see Pierre so heartened and once again she let herself be carried away by the enthusiasm of her family.

The winter was busy. The men cut down trees to clear their land and to use for firewood. There were plans to cultivate the land and bring in farm animals the following spring. They hoped to grow wheat. And there were good prospects for shipbuilding.

—

At the end of their first fishing season in Chétican, Joseph Richard dit Matinal and his family left to go to settle at Tracadie on St. George's Bay. His wife Marguerite's health was failing and he believed that the conditions at Chétican were too harsh for her. Jeanne was sorry to see them leave; Joseph, her second cousin, had been the only relative still part of her daily life.

Their departure made her realize that she had not spent much time thinking of her brothers since she and Pierre had been released from Georges Island. She had heard from fellow Acadians that Joseph had been deported from Saint-Pierre et Miquelon to France, but had heard nothing of Charles or Abraham. It was a source of sorrow for her, but their absence from her life now was not the urgent pain of earlier years.

She had another family now, not just her children and grandchildren, but the whole group of Acadians in their new community, where Jeanne knew she would be needed again in her role of midwife and comforter of the sick. From time to time Mi'kmaq came to visit, greeting them as friends. Several of them knew of the Dugas family, mainly because of Jeanne's brother Joseph. This brought back memories to Jeanne, but she did not mention Martin Sauvage; so much time had passed.

Jeanne sensed that it was the breaking up of families and family ties that had dealt the strongest blow to the spirit of the Acadians and wondered if it could be built up again for those who chose to remain on this land.

—

The little community of Chétican grew. They were soon joined by a group of Acadians who came from Île Saint-Jean. After the fall of Louisbourg, they had either been deported or fled the island to go to the Miramichi. When they returned to the island in the late 1760s, they found that Île Saint-Jean had been divided into sixty-seven cantons that were given to absentee British landlords. The Acadian settlers were considered tenants and had to pay a rental fee for the use of the land. Needless to say, this was impossible. In some cases, they had not been made aware of the situation, finding out only when they were asked to pay an exorbitant fee at the end of a season's hard work.

Others shared their stories. A man who had been deported and crossed the Atlantic on the *Mary* said that at least 250 of the 560 Acadians it carried died, most of them children, for want of "the necessities of life." Another ship, the *Ruby*, was blown off course and ran aground – only 120 of the 310 Acadians on board were rescued. Two other ships, the *Violet* and the *Duke William*, sank along with their passengers. For those who survived the voyages, the conditions they met when they arrived at their destinations were horrific. It was believed that almost 2,000 Acadians died during the deportations from Île Saint-Jean.

Pierre Aucoin and his brother Joseph, both born in Acadia, had been deported to Virginia in 1755. When that colony refused to accept them, they were sent on to England and imprisoned in barracks on the docks of London. When released and sent to France in 1763, only about 350 of the original 1500 prisoners had survived. Most had succumbed to cold, hunger and sickness – many of them were children.

Grégoire Maillet had fled Grand-Pré before the Deportation of 1755, but had been captured and deported to France on the same ship as Joseph Deveau.

Joseph Boudreau had been born in France, where his parents had eventually been sent after being refused asylum in Virginia and then imprisoned in England. They arrived in France in 1763, where Joseph was born two years later. He was only twenty-one years old when he arrived in Chétican.

The Aucoin, Maillet, Deveau and Boudreau families had all returned to Acadia from France on the Robin company ships in 1773. Chased from the Gaspé peninsula by colonial privateers, like the Bois family and their group, they had then travelled from pillar to post seeking a permanent refuge. Some of them had spent years on Saint-Pierre et Miquelon.

While Jeanne and Pierre Bois and their group, as well as Paul, Basile and Jean Chiasson and Lazard Leblanc, had not been deported, they had equally harrowing stories to tell of their escapes, their imprisonment and their losses.

All the stories revolved around the sea. The sea had been their means of transport, their means of escape and their means of earning a living when circumstances made them fishermen rather than farmers. It had inspired their songs and their culture. But the sea had also been their enemy. The sea had brought war and displacement. It had wrenched them from their homes, and had deported them to foreign lands – often it had been their burial ground. Jeanne understood and shared this strong attachment the Acadians had to the sea. She felt it in the very marrow of her bones.

Each year a few more seekers of asylum came to Chétican. By 1790, there were twenty-six Acadian families in the new settlement.

Chapter 45

In 1784, Cap Breton Island had become a separate and distinct province in the new British colony and the provincial authorities were willing to give land grants to returning Acadians. The authorities wanted the Acadians to settle here to prevent them from strengthening the French presence in Saint-Pierre et Miquelon and to prevent them from competing with the English trade there.

Pierre Bois was determined that they should obtain title to the land they had settled.

In the spring of 1788 he recruited four of the earliest settlers and set off for Sydney to approach the governor with a written request for title to their land. His son, Régis, who had written the letter, accompanied them. Régis was for some years the only man in Chétican who could read and write and became the unofficial clerk for the new settlement. Jeanne asked God to forgive her for the sin of pride, for she was indeed very proud of both her husband and her son.

On September 20, 1790, a Charter was signed by the authority of William Maccormic, lieutenant and commander-in-chief of the province of Cap Breton, granting a total of

7,000 arpents of land to fourteen of the Acadian settlers at Chétican.

The fourteen men who carefully drew an "X" beside their names as they appeared on the grant were: Pierre Bois, Pierre Aucoin, Joseph Boudreau, Joseph Gaudet, Paul Chiasson, Basile Chiasson, Joseph Deveau, Grégoire Maillet, Jean Chiasson, Lazard Leblanc, Raymond Poirier, Anselme Aucoin, Joseph Aucoin and Augustin Deveau. Pierre Bois's name was at the head of the list and for many years the grant was known as "la grant à Pierre Bois," and rightly so, for he had been the prime mover in obtaining it.

—

Jeanne knew that if the men arrived with the grant in hand it would be a victory and a milestone for their small Acadian village. They had been confident they would obtain the grant, so the women of Chétican had prepared a feast to welcome them back.

By mid-afternoon, when everything was ready, Jeanne returned to her home alone and, during a few moments of quiet and repose, took time to reflect on her life and her community.

She was approaching her sixtieth year. She had spent most of her life like a sailor without a home port – now her children would have a real home. In five years, they had helped to create an Acadian village out of the wilderness, built a homestead, made improvements to the basic log house built so hastily on their arrival. They had acquired an ox and a few farm animals and then increased their stock and built a barn and a shed; there was plentiful grass and hay for the animals. They had milk and eggs and fresh meat again. They planted a kitchen garden that became larger each year.

The men hunted moose for its meat and hides, and other smaller animals to supplement their food supplies. They had sheep for wool and they planted flax for linen. The women were busy all winter spinning and weaving and knitting. They made maple sugar in the spring as they had learned to do from the Mi'kmaq. They planted tobacco for the men to smoke in their pipes. They made soap, candles, moccasins and remedies from plants. And they had pure fresh water from their stream.

They had learned to live to the rhythm of nature in their new community, enjoying the mild climate afforded by their nearness to the sea and coping with the violent storms that came with it. They had learned the signs that announced the arrival of a suête (southeast) gale-force wind. Fishermen at sea would head for home port and everything at home would be secured while they rode out the storm. The suête was as frightening and potentially as destructive as heavy thunder and lightning.

Two years after their arrival, Jeanne had delivered Frédérick – a son for Augustin Deveau and Rose Richard – the first baby to be born in Chétican. Jeanne wrapped him in her beautiful embroidered shawl when she baptized him, and asked la bonne Sainte-Anne to protect him. They had no clergy in these early years, but Joseph Aucoin, somewhere on his travels, had received the Church's authority to perform "white ceremonies," and he served as their elder. They would gather at Augustin Deveau's house, which was central, to sing hymns and sometimes even simple folk songs, and recite the prayers they had learned so long ago. Joseph Aucoin performed the "white marriages" and he had agreed with Jeanne that she should baptize the newborns.

And now, Jeanne fervently hoped, they would be legally entitled to this land and its bounty, and to the bounty of the sea. She was grateful too for the friendship of the Mi'kmaq.

They had always been a part of her and her brother Joseph's lives. It was comforting to have them nearby. And it helped to keep Martin's memory alive.

In a nostalgic mood, she took out the statuette of Sainte-Anne, the embroidered shawl with Mère Saint-Joseph's initials on it, and her portrait in the blue silk gown still kept in the woven-grass pouch Martin had made. *Who was that young girl in the portrait?* she wondered.

—

There was great excitement when the men arrived, waving the land-grant in the air. They also had several small kegs of rum, which they took turns carrying. They had obviously been tippling on their way. The whole community gathered and they ate and drank and talked and talked, and talked some more. They made music and sang and danced – it was a wonderful Acadian soirée.

When Jeanne and Pierre returned to their house, Pierre saw Jeanne's portrait in the blue silk gown lying on the table. "Ah, Jeanne," he said, "I remember when I first saw this portrait of you, before we got married. I fell in love with you then. Ever since, when I look at you, this is how you always look to me." Jeanne smiled; it was amazing, she thought, what a little rum could do.

Chapter 46

There seemed to be a change in Jeanne's inner life, or character, in the years following the receipt of the land grant. She recognized it in herself and was not sure what brought it about, seeing it as a weakness. Was it the fact that she was no longer constantly living on tenterhooks, waiting for the next war, the next displacement, the next disaster? Was it just her age? After all, she was now over sixty and surely could make a claim of weariness. Or was it simply that when she looked on the portrait of herself as the young woman in blue she wondered what her life might have been if events had unfolded differently? And she wondered whether she had done everything she could to help others and herself in the life she had been dealt.

Then there was the melancholy that she felt living in the valley of Le Platin out of sight of the sea. She had spent so much time on and near the sea, and had been comfortable on ships, where she had felt a sense of freedom and adventure. Even when they had lived in places where they did not want to be seen from the sea, she had been able to look out on it. But their home in Chétican was landlocked. On dull, grey days she felt oppressed by the mountain on one side, the hill on the other and the dark sky looming above.

She could not discuss her feelings with anyone, but Pierre surely knew she had changed. He was aware that she missed the sea and he asked her if she would like to go sailing one day and where she would like to go.

"Ah, Pierre, yes, I would" she smiled. "You know, I think I'd like to go and see what is left of Louisbourg. I was thinking of it just the other day."

True to his word, on a sunny autumn day, Pierre sailed with Jeanne and Régis to the old town. By the time they arrived, grey clouds had gathered and the air was cool and damp. It was ominous.

Jeanne knew that the British had destroyed the town, but she had not expected such a complete physical devastation. The wharves were in ruins. The proud stone buildings that had once housed the governor, the militia, the elites, the hospital and the convent were reduced to rubble. There was an eerie silence, except for the wind whispering like a host of ghosts, where once there had been such a loud hubbub of activity. Vegetation was ruthlessly taking over wherever it could. It was difficult to even make out where some streets had been.

The only living being here now was a solitary man dressed in shabby black clothes sitting on a stone block some distance away. He did not approach them. *Mon Dieu*, Jeanne thought, *What has become of the bustling port, the governor, the militia, the merchants, the missionaries, the nuns, the music teachers, the dancing masters, the laundresses, the artist who painted my portrait, the workers who tended the cod flakes?*

Jeanne had trouble orienting herself in what was now a strange landscape. Her face looked drawn and dazed. Pierre and Régis exchanged worried looks. She had not uttered a word since they had arrived, but they did not want to break her silence. She started to walk inland and they followed her. Finally, she stopped in front of what was left of a partly destroyed building. She turned to her husband and son.

"I wanted to show you my father's house, where I was born, but.... But nothing is where I am sure it should be." She spoke falteringly. "I believe this is what's left of my stepfather's house. Imagine, Monsieur de la Tour's house had an elegant parlour, with a clavecin, and a tapestry with beautiful shepherdesses in it hanging on the wall. My sister Angélique was in love with both the clavecin and the shepherdesses. Poor Angélique."

"I'm sorry, Jeanne."

"No, Pierre. Don't be." She shook her head. "I wanted to come and I'm glad I did."

She took a final look at the ruins around her. *Mais, mon Dieu. Ah, mon Dieu.*

"There are only ghosts here. I'd like to go home, Pierre."

"Come, Jeanne." Pierre put his arm around her and she slid her arm around his back as they slowly walked down to the harbour together. Régis followed them at a short distance as he tried to imagine his mother's life in the once-great fortress and what his parents and especially his mother, had suffered through since then.

As they sailed away and rounded the cape, the sun came out again.

—

Jeanne and Pierre's family grew. In 1792, Régis married Apolline Arsenault, and two years later Geneviève married Maximilien Gaudet. With their two younger children now married and settled in homes of their own nearby, Jeanne and Pierre had an empty nest. Jeanne had convinced Pierre that there was no need for him to work as hard, and he was now fishing on a reduced scale with his son Régis.

Jeanne herself was letting go of some activities. Her daughter Marie was taking over her mother's duties as the village midwife. All the early babies in Chétican had been baptized in the embroidered shawl and under the protection of Sainte-Anne, and Marie continued the tradition. Marie's daughter Eulalie was the apple of her grandmother Jeanne's eye. Eulalie, married to a son of Augustin Deveau, was beginning to follow in her mother and grandmother's footsteps.

Chapter 47

In the summer of 1805, Jeanne noticed that her husband's health was failing. Pierre's movements were slow and he sometimes looked confused, though he refused to stop working. Jeanne urged Régis to keep an eye on his father when they were at sea.

Jeanne felt such an outpouring of love for him in these later years – this small man with his rolling sailor's gait, now bent with age. His whole life had been wrapped up in his love for his wife and children. He had been a good father and now a good grandfather. Jeanne could not imagine her life without him. But le bon Dieu came for him in the autumn, when the trees were at their most defiant with colour. At least they had had time to talk. She, about her love for him – he, about his concern for her when he was gone. He was buried in the new cemetery on the side of the hill, with his back to the sea, facing toward the mountains and the sky, which Jeanne in her heart knew was all wrong.

Jeanne refused to leave her home and her children could not bear the thought of her being there alone, so it was agreed that her favourite granddaughter Eulalie and her husband Jean Baptiste Deveau would live with her.

—

On a beautiful morning the following summer, as Jeanne was weeding her garden, she saw Marie coming to see her. There was a man with her, but Jeanne's eyesight was failing and she did not recognize him from a distance, although she thought that by his erect walk and the way he held himself that he was probably a Mi'kmaw. It was only when he came closer to her that she realized she was looking at—

Martin? My Martin? Am I dreaming? Am I losing my mind? But there he was, her young, handsome Martin.

"Martin?" she asked softly and hesitantly.

"No, Maman Jeanne," he smiled. "My name is Joseph-Martin. I am Martin's son."

"Ah, mon Dieu! Mon Dieu!" She held out her arms to him and hugged him as tears ran down her cheeks

"Maman Jeanne, please don't cry," he said. "I am so happy to see you."

"But I am crying because I am so happy to see *you*." She smiled through her tears. "You look just like your father. Ah, mon Dieu. How did Marie find you? Or how did you find me?"

"I heard there was a sister of Joseph Dugas here and I thought it must be you. It was my great-uncle Jean Sauvage who told me about you and your family. And about how my father was your friend. I was very young when my father died, but my great-uncle Jean told me stories about him when I was a small boy."

"Marie, you remember Martin, don't you?"

"Yes, of course, Maman. I knew him when I was just a little girl. I used to call him Uncle Martin. He told me once that he was the first person in the world to set eyes on me when I was born. I knew him as a wonderful man. And Maman is right, Joseph-Martin, you look just like him."

Jeanne brought him into the house and happily chatted with him about his life and his family. Marie did not interrupt; she was happy to see her mother so animated. Joseph-Martin shared the noon meal with the two women and he seemed to be as taken with Jeanne as she was with him.

They talked about the fate of the Acadians and the Mi'kmaq. He asked if Jeanne and her family were happy to be in Chétican.

"Well," said Jeanne, "we finally have a home. We have been granted title to this land. It's good not to have to face the possibility of being uprooted each spring. We spent so many winters worrying about 'what news spring would bring' and wondering if we would have to sail away again. You know, I still find myself slipping into the same thoughts each winter and sometimes I even dream about it."

"You've never mentioned this before," said Marie.

"I know, Marie. But it's true."

As Joseph-Martin was leaving, Jeanne asked him to come to visit again and he promised he would.

Then she remembered the statuette. "Wait," she said, "I want to show you something."

She brought him the statuette of Sainte-Anne.

"Your father gave me this," she told him, "She's beautiful, isn't she?"

"Yes," said Joseph-Martin, looking at the statuette and then back at Jeanne. "She looks like you." He saw that she was startled. "Had you not noticed?"

"Mon Dieu." Jeanne felt her tears coming again.

Joseph-Martin gave her his father's beautiful smile and quietly slipped away.

Chapter 48

In 1812, during Jeanne's eightieth year, the Bishop of Québec, Joseph-Octave Plessis, came to Chétican as part of his pastoral visit to the Catholic missions in the golfe du Saint-Laurent.

As one of the respected elders in the community, and a midwife and healer, Jeanne received a visit from the Bishop. He sat in her home and accepted a cup of herbal tea, as she told him of the years she and her family had spent evading the British, of their travels, and of how they had managed to escape deportation. And she told him that during all that time they had never gone to bed without supper.

The Bishop was very impressed. "Madame," he said, "what a difficult life you have led. I am sure that our good Lord will prepare a special place for you in heaven. It is wonderful to see how you strong Acadian women achieved such a noble survival."

Jeanne struggled to put a look of appropriate womanly submission on her face. She knelt when the Bishop gave her his blessing and left.

She watched his black back recede as he was led away to make his next visit. Only then did she let the thoughts rush to the surface, giving the good Bishop a silent piece of her mind.

Yes, my good Bishop, how nice to have a place in heaven. But how can I believe that, when le bon Dieu did not see fit to let us have a small plot of land here on earth where we can live in peace? Once again our lives are threatened by the effects of yet another war.

You believe that we Acadian women survived because we were strong? No, that's not how it happened. Those of us who survived became strong in the struggle. It wasn't so much that we fought for survival; it was more a question of how much we could endure. And we were able to do it not for ourselves, but for our children. That was our survival. There was nothing noble about that.

And what about the brave women and children among us who did not survive? Are they less worthy, less noble? Does their suffering count for nothing? Will they simply be forgotten?

I told you one small lie by omission my good Bishop. It is true that we never went to bed without some food in our stomachs, but there were many nights when my children and I went to bed hungry because of too little food. My pride made me hide the truth.

Jeanne realized that for only the second time in her life she had let herself be overwhelmed by anger. The first time – many years ago, in a moment of despair – she had been able to spit her anger out loud to Martin, that night in the woods. But she could not do that with the good Bishop.

Ah, mon Dieu, I should have knelt before him and confessed all my angry thoughts. Would he have taken away my special place in heaven and sent me straight to hell? Well, so be it, for at times I think I have already been there.

—

The War of 1812 was over in three years, and although the Chéticantins were not directly affected, Jeanne and others of her generation had felt the weight of it over their heads. And because it worried Jeanne, her children worried about her.

It was clear that her health was failing, although Jeanne continued to work in her garden as long as she could. She visited with her children and grandchildren and Joseph-Martin brought his family to visit more often. She enjoyed seeing his children and grandchildren as much as her own.

In the winter of 1817, Jeanne was bedridden. She did not seem to be suffering from a specific malady, but rather was simply wasting away. Marie spent most of her time at her bedside. Jeanne knew she was instinctively passing on her mantle to her daughter and that Marie was accepting it silently.

Jeanne lived through spring and into summer. As summer drew to its end, she called Marie, Régis, Geneviève and Eulalie to her bedside. Their worried faces gathered around her.

"No, I'm not dying yet," said Jeanne. "But I have something serious to ask of you."

"Yes, of course, Maman." Marie spoke for all of them.

"Listen my children, when I do go, I want to be buried at sea."

There was a soft involuntary gasp from Marie and then total silence.

"Eh bien?"

Régis, aghast, looked at Marie. His sister remained silent for a few moments. Jeanne watched different emotions move across her daughter's face. No one said a word.

Then Marie smiled. "Yes, of course, Maman, if that is what you truly want."

"Yes, that is what I truly want. Thank you, Marie, my big girl."

—

A few weeks later, as the first leaves were starting to turn co-lour, Jeanne Dugas passed away in her eighty-seventh year. The family held the usual veillée at her home, where the whole village and the surrounding communities paid their respects. Then they kept Maman's body at the house one more night, with only the family in attendance. To Marie's great relief, the priest was away on a pastoral visit.

Early the next morning, Joseph-Martin arrived with two large canoes paddled by Mi'kmaw warriors. The family were waiting for him. A solemn Marie stood clutching the grass pouch containing her young Maman's portrait.

Joseph-Martin had brought a small bouquet of sweet grass and herbs tied with a ribbon, which he placed beside Maman's body. Marie very hesitantly added the grass pouch. Her heart ached at the thought of letting it go forever, but she felt it was important for her mother to have it with her. It completed the story of her life.

Joseph-Martin helped the family to wrap Jeanne's body in her best blanket and then in the animal-skin shroud he had brought. The warriors carried her down to the shore and put her in one of the canoes. Joseph-Martin accompanied them.

Marie, Régis, Geneviève, Eulalie and their spouses, to-gether with Joseph-Martin's family, followed in the second canoe.

They seemed to travel a great distance. When they stopped, they were out of sight of land. The sea was calm, there was no wind, the air was warm and moist. But Marie could feel the strength and power of the sea surging under the boats. The two canoes drew close. No one uttered a word.

A Mi'kmaw elder in the first canoe stood and said a short prayer in his native tongue, accompanied by a softly muffled drum. The warriors then lifted Jeanne's body and very gently lowered it into the sea.

Geneviève and Eulalie wept softly. Marie was dry-eyed, but could not speak. She sent a silent message to her mother Jeanne Dugas. *Go in peace, Maman. You no longer have to worry about what news spring will bring.*

What Became of...

Charles Dugas, not taken captive in the MacKenzie raid because he was ill, left Nipisiguit about a month later. He took his wife and children to settle in Tracadièche (now Carleton, QC). One of his sons, Joseph, married a daughter of Alexis Landry and they eventually settled in Caraquet, NB. Joseph and his father-in-law were among the Acadians who obtained land in Caraquet under a government grant similar to that given to the settlers of Chétican. Charles Dugas died in Tracadièche in 1801 at the age of ninety. Many of his descendants can be found there and in Caraquet today.

Joseph Dugas, after his escape from Georges Island in 1762 to hide in Chedabouctou, emigrated to St. Pierre et Miquelon two years later. His marriage to Louise Arsenault was rehabilitated there in 1766. In November 1767, as a result of French policy, he was deported to France, only to be forced to return to St. Pierre et Miquelon the following spring. In 1778, when the British captured St. Pierre et Miquelon, Joseph Dugas was again deported to France. He lived his last years in penury and died in Saint-Servant in 1779 at the age of sixty-five. His wife died five months later.

Abraham Dugas escaped Georges Island with his brother Joseph and followed him to Chedabouctou, St. Pierre et Miquelon, France and back to St. Pierre et Miquelon. He then remained on this continent. He and his family are believed to have spent some time in Newfoundland and they were settled in the area of Clare, NS, by 1772, where many of his descendants can be found today. This is the area where the first land grants were given to Acadians after the end of the Seven Years War; it is now known as the French Shore.

Joseph Leblanc dit Le Maigre left Georges Island in 1763. He followed Joseph Dugas to St. Pierre et Miquelon and he too was deported to France in 1767. He settled in Belle-Île-en-Mer, in the village of Kerval with other Acadian refugees and died there in 1772.

Charles des Champs de Boishébert was involved in the last battles in New France in 1759 and 1760. After the fall of Montréal, he retreated to France, where he was imprisoned in the Bastille, accused of having profited personally from the purchase of supplies for the starving Acadians. He was acquitted after serving fifteen months in prison. He spent his last years in France at Raffetot, an estate he acquired through marriage, where he died in 1797.

Brief Glossary

un aboiteau - dyke system that allows reclaimed marshland to be farmed

le cabotage - coastal navigation

un caboteur - a coastal navigator

charpente construction - timber frame with rubble stone infill.

un clavecin - harpsichord

Compagnies franches de la Marine - the main organization for the defence of New France

un concordat - agreement

un conte - fairy tale

à contre-gré - against one's will

la layette - baby clothes

Lettres de Marques - licence to arm a vessel, engage and capture merchant ships that otherwise would be piracy

une paillasse - straw mattress

une pastorelle - story in verse on pastoral themes

un piquet - vertical log construction

une sage-femme - midwife

une soirée - party

têtu - stubborn

une veillée - vigil, wake

Place names

No longer in use or changed:

Baie Française, now the Bay of Fundy
Camp de l'Ésperance, an Island in Miramichi Bay, NB
Canceau, now Canso, NS
Chédabouctou, near Canso, NS
Chétican, now Chéticamp, NS
Chezzetcook, Halifax, Co., NS
Chipagon, Shippagan, NB
La Petite Rochelle, on Miramichi Bay, NB
Magré, Margaree, Cap Breton, NS
Miré, Mira bay and river and village, Cap Breton, NS
Neireishak, now Arichat, Isle Madame, NS
Nipisiguit, now Bathurst, NB
Port-la-Joye, Prince Edward Island
Port Toulouse/Potlotek, St. Peter's, Cap Breton, NS
Remshic, now Wallace, NS
Richibuctu, Richibouctou, NB
Ristigouche, Restigouche, NB
Havre Hébert, Les Îles-de-la-Madeleine, Québec

About the author

Photo by Tim Snow

Cassie Deveaux Cohoon was born in the Acadian village of Chétican on Cap Breton Island, Nova Scotia. Her Acadian heritage goes back to the early days of Grand Pré on her father's side and Beaubassin (now Amherst) on her mother's. She has lived in New York City and Paris, France, and now makes her home in Montréal, Québec. She has worked as a freelance journalist and written family histories. Her first novel, *Severine*, told the story of a fictitious heroine of Acadia. In *Jeanne Dugas of Acadia*, the author tells the story of one of her own ancestors. One of Jeanne Dugas's granddaughters married a son of Augustin Deveau, another founder of Chétican and the author's paternal ancestor.